THE
POWER SLAM
GRAMMAR BOOK

THE POWER SLAM GRAMMAR BOOK

Alison Kooistra
&
John Kooistra

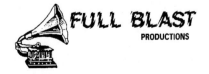

IN CANADA   IN THE UNITED STATES

FB Productions   FB Productions
Box 408   Box 1297
Virgil, Ontario   Lewiston, New York 14092-8297
L0S 1T0

Phone: 905-468-7558
Fax: 905-468-5706
E-mail: fbp@vaxxine.com
Website: www.fullblastproductions.com

National Library of Canada Cataloguing in Publication Data

Kooistra, John Peter, 1953-
    The power slam grammar book

ISBN 1-895451-41-8

1. English Language -- Grammar--Problems, exercises, etc.
I. Kooistra, Alison, 1979- II. Title.

PE1112.K665 2001   428.2' 076   C2001-903134-3

Printed in Canada.

ISBN 1-895451-41-8

The Power Slam Grammar Book

The sequel to the highly successful *Power Drill Grammar Book* for intermediate students, *The Power Slam Grammar Book* addresses the needs of senior grade school students (age 11 and higher). Every lesson in this book begins with the premise that, contrary to prevailing prejudices, language instruction can be the most profitable, pleasurable and exciting period in a student's day. The lessons vary from individual to group work, from written to oral work, and from serious reflection to "wild and crazy" fun — although every lesson is productive and valuable.

Why should your classroom have a copy of this book?
It's fun — many of the lessons are in the form of games, and the practice sentences reflect everybody's interest in movies, computers, video games, dating, sports, and all the popular social activities of the early 21st Century.

It's practical — the exercises focus on students' primary needs: error correction of their writing and speech, and expansion of their range of expression, without requiring the memorizing of grammar terminology. The six units focus on parts of speech, sentence construction (statements, negations, questions, answers, and commands), usage problems, and a range of verb tenses (present, past, future). Instruction for each verb tense is also accompanied by an excellent pictorial representation of that tense — helping to simplify the complexities of tense, mood and aspect. Furthermore, every unit concludes with a detailed composition exercise that builds on and reinforces the foregoing grammar lessons.

Finally, *The Power Slam Grammar Book* is an excellent, high-energy *complement* to instructional material for the analysis of literature and popular media. Teachers or students can use it as either a required text or an aid in any English, ESL or EFL classroom.

John & Alison Kooistra

A Message to Students

Hello! My name is Alison. I am 22 years old and the co-author of this book. When I was in school I hated it. Most of the work seemed repetitive, boring and pointless. I couldn't understand why I was being forced against my will to attend class and do homework. School didn't seem to have any application in the "real world." I had the impression that whatever I did inside school would not have an impact on my life after graduation.

I was wrong. Although I had felt powerless, I realized after I graduated high school that I had been making powerful choices all the time. Although students are lawfully forced to attend school, they cannot be forced to understand or remember information. You can refuse to do homework. You can refuse to listen. You can refuse to think. But in the end, these decisions will harm you and hurt your chances for a successful life.

As my father and I wrote this book, we tried to make the lessons as interesting and as fun as possible. We also wanted them to be something more for you than exercises that you can take or leave. The thing is, just doing the exercises isn't enough — you also need to think about them. Learning is a choice.

So, why *should* you bother to learn grammar rules? What's the point?

The point is communication. Clear communication is a skill that you will need to apply to all areas of your life, both personal and professional. Whether you're applying for a job, writing an essay for high school or college, typing an e-mail to a business contact, or trying to find the right words to convince someone to go out with you, the ability to form coherent sentences is vital.

So — think about how much time you have, and how much energy. Think about where you would like to be two or five or ten years from now. Then think about the fact that you've got two or five or ten years to work on your communication skills, and that with any luck you'll have some fun doing the hard work that you have to do.

Remember, the point of school is to help prepare you for life, for the outside world. Instead of letting your school use you, you can use your school (and books like this one) to get to where you want to go. Good luck!

Alison Kooistra

TABLE OF CONTENTS

UNIT ONE — SENTENCE STRUCTURE

UNIT TWO — QUESTIONS, QUOTATIONS and PRONOUNS

UNIT THREE — COMMANDS and DICTION

UNIT FOUR — PRESENT TIME

UNIT FIVE — PAST TIME

UNIT SIX — FUTURE TIME

UNIT ONE — SENTENCE STRUCTURE

INTRODUCTION: THE PARTS OF SPEECH

Everything you see or use is made up of parts. A basic computer, for example, can be broken down into parts: a hard drive, a motherboard, RAM, a keyboard, a mouse, and so on. Each part relies on the other to make the computer run properly. You do not have to know the names of ALL parts of the computer to know how to use it efficiently. However, it helps to know the basic parts when you need something fixed, or when you want upgrades.

A sentence works in essentially the same way. Each word in every sentence comes from one of ten basic categories of words. We give you a short list below. Don't worry! As this book goes on, we won't be trying to load you down with thousands of boring and confusing grammar terms. You don't need to know all the names in order to speak and write good English; however, it is valuable to learn some of the most basic terms when you are trying to fix an error or to upgrade your language skills.

Another way to use the descriptions in the following few pages is as a reference guide. In later exercises, when words such as "noun" or "adverb" or "conjunction" are used, you can simply find their definitions right here.

1. Noun: A noun is a word that names a person, place or thing.

> Person: John, woman, Mary, grandmother, brother, acrobat, telemarketer.
> Place: city, field, gymnasium, classroom, mall, China.
> Thing: stick, bat, shoe, purse, motorcycle, cat, monkey.

Proper vs. common nouns: in the above list, several nouns begin with capital letters. They are proper nouns. All the rest are common nouns.

Proper nouns begin with capital letters, and name a specific person (Joe), country (United States), pet (Fluffy), month (April), day (Monday), store (Gap), etc. They are also used for job titles (President Bush, Principal Skinner).

Countable vs. Noncountable nouns: most nouns are countable — they have a singular and a plural form (one cat, two cats; a song, two songs). You can put an "a" or "an" in front of them, and you can add an "s" or "es" to them in the plural form.

Noncountable nouns usually cannot have "a" or "an" in front of them, and you cannot add "s" or "es" to them (examples: music, information, weather, money, homework).

Some noncountable nouns are sometimes called "mass nouns." These describe things that have many individual parts, but are treated as singular nouns. Two examples are "sugar" and "coffee." There are many grains of sugar in a bowl and many grains of coffee in a jar, but we say "The sugar **is** in the bowl" (not **are** in the bowl), and "The coffee **is** in the jar."

1

2. Pronoun: A pronoun is a word that is used in the place of a noun. The following pronouns are the ones we use most often:

		SINGULAR					PLURAL	
(a)	I	you	she	he	it	we	you	they
(b)	me	you	her	him	it	us	you	them
(c)	my	your	her	his	its	our	your	their
(d)	mine	yours	hers	his		ours	yours	theirs

— Reflexive pronouns

myself, yourself, herself, himself, itself .... ourselves ..... yourselves ... themselves

— Demonstrative pronouns: this, that, these those.

These four words have different names in different sentences. They are called "pronouns" in sentences such as "**Those** are mine" or "Give me **that**."

They are usually called "limiting adjectives" in sentences such as "**Those books** are mine" or "Give me **that book**" (because they are followed immediately by a noun).

3. Verb: A verb usually shows action, showing what someone or something *does* in the past, present, or future. A verb can also show what someone or something *is* or *has*.

> ran, run, running, will run   acted, act, acting, will act
> was, is, being, will be   had, has, having, will have

Another important type of verb is the "modal helping verb". These verbs add the ideas of *possibility*, *responsibility*, or *ability* to another verb in a sentence:

> could, should, would, may, might, can, must, shall…

Example: Jack **should open** the door for that old lady. (The main verb is "open"; the helping or "modal" verb is "should", indicating Jack's responsibility).

4. Adjective: Adjectives are words that describe nouns or pronouns. They describe size, weight, age, color, emotion, intelligence, beauty, number and many other qualities.

> huge, tiny, light, young, old, black, yellow, happy, curious, intelligent, smart, brilliant, handsome, gorgeous, ten (10), twenty (20)…

Some adjectives look like verbs, and are spelled with an "-ed," "-en" or "-ing."

Examples: defeated, frightened, beaten, broken, running, flying…
Used in phrases such as "the *defeated* team," "the *broken* play," "the *flying* squirrel."

2

5. Adverb: Adverbs are words that describe everything that an adjective does not describe. Most adverbs describe the place, direction, time, frequency, and manner of the action in a sentence. In general, you could say that they describe the **time** when something happens, the **place** where something happens, and **how** something happens.

Place: here, there, home, away, upstairs… [Lassie walked **home**]

Direction: sideways, directly, up, down… [The giant looked **down**]

Time: yesterday, today, suddenly, now… [The Lakers won **yesterday**]

Frequency: always, never, sometimes… [The Red Sox **never** win the World Series]

Intensifiers: very, truly, definitely… [Eminem will **definitely** win an Emmy]

Manner: quickly, lazily, crazily, happily… [Rap singers talk **quickly**]

6. Conjunction: Conjunctions are words that connect other words or phrases or sentences. The most common conjunctions are: "and", "or", "but".

Another type of conjunction is usually used to join a pair of sentences together; "however", "moreover", "nevertheless" and "therefore" are several examples (and are sometimes called "conjunctive adverbs").

"Shaquille is a great basketball player. **However**, he is a bad free throw shooter."
(or, change the first period to a semicolon)
"Shaquille is a great basketball player**;** **however**, he is a bad free throw shooter."

Another type of conjunction is usually used to link a dependent clause to the main sentence. Several examples are "because", "although", "when", "while" and "where" (and are often called "subordinating conjunctions").

"Mariah went to the store **because** she wanted a bag of Gummy Bears."

7. Preposition: Prepositions are words that connect a noun or pronoun to another element in a sentence.

Examples: for, to, by, in, out, with, between, from, off, on.

Prepositions usually form the beginnings of prepositional phrases, such as "**in** the room", "**off** the rebound", "**for** my brothers and sisters", "**from** the heart"…

8. Article: A small group of words — **a, an, the** — used in front of nouns.

Examples: "**a** game", "**an** event" — "a" and "an" are called *indefinite articles*, because they describe a game or event that is not specific. "An" is used instead of "a" in front of nouns that begin with a vowel (a, e, i, o, u — "an apple"; "an eye for an eye"; "an opening").

"The" is a *definite article*: in a phrase such as "**the** game", a specific, definite game is described.

9. Interjection: "Interjection" means to "throw into"-- these are words that we throw into sentences (or between sentences) when we're excited or angry or surprised. We do not usually use them in the kinds of writing that we do for our parents or teachers.

Examples: hey, um, uh, ouch! Huh? Doh!

Homer Simpson said, "**Hey**, Mr. Burns, could I, **uh**, take the whole year off work? **Doh!**"

{**10. Particle:** There is only one little word in this category -- it looks like a preposition, but it actually does not have much of a meaning in its own right. It is the **"to"** at the beginning of something that is called an **"infinitive verb phrase,"** such as **"to think"**, **"to do"**, **"to be**, or not **to be"**...}

* * * * *

*Note to teachers and students:

In any exercise where you are asked to identify the parts of speech, as in **A1** on the next page, some words will cause trouble. As mentioned above, a word such as "this," for example, can act like a pronoun in a sentence such as "I like **this**," but it is more like an article or adjective in a sentence such as "**This** book is mine." In this case, you are not wrong if you call it a pronoun (specifically a "demonstrative pronoun"), an adjective (a "limiting adjective"), or even an article (like an even more specific "the").

Don't get too fussy about the right names when you find these odd, border-crossing words. Keep in mind that knowing the parts of speech is mainly valuable as a guide in getting larger groups of words into their correct form and order.

Lesson 1 — The Parts of Speech

Exercise A. Read pages 1 to 4. Next, identify the parts of speech in the following sentences. You may use abbreviations for each word ("adj" for "adjective"), or you may simply use the numbers from the list above.

Noun = N or 1.   Pronoun = Pron or 2.   Verb = V or 3.
Adjective = Adj or 4.   Adverb = Adv or 5.   Conjunction = Con or 6.
Preposition = Prep or 7. Article = Art or 8   Interjection = Int or 9
{Particle = Pa or 10}

Example:

A	team	of	troopers	travelled	quickly	to	Mars,
(Art)	(N)	(Prep)	(N)	(Vb)	(Adv)	(Prep)	(N)

and	they	began	a	violent	attack	on	the	aliens.
(Con)	(Pro)	(Vb)	(Art)	(Adj)	(N)	(Prep)	(Art)	(N)

1. Orleanna spent a long, hot day at the beach.

2. Kandi is happy because she won a free computer.

3. The principal was thoughtful while she decided the fate of the students.

4. Go quickly to the store and buy three ripe, green apples for me.

5. Wanda and Wendy plan to climb a mountain next weekend.

6. Raoul truly likes to program games on his computer.

7. Hey — this apple pie is delicious.

8. A child laughs approximately 400 times in a day; however, an adult laughs

   only 15 times.   {note: the numbers in this sentence are adjectives}

Exercise B. Write down a sentence that you remember from one of your favorite TV shows (or make up a sentence that a favorite actor is likely to say). Your sentence should be at least seven words long, and it should have words that won't embarrass anyone. Exchange your sentence with a partner. Try to name all the parts of speech correctly, then compare notes with your partner. If there are any words you can't identify, ask your teacher.

_____

_____

Lesson 2 — What is a sentence?

The parts of speech are organized into larger patterns in order to form sentences. Most sentences have three basic elements:

a beginning, a verb (or group of verbs), and an ending.

The beginning is usually called the subject of the sentence. The subject is the **"who"** or the **"what"** that **does** (or **is** or **has**) something in the sentence.

The verb element in a sentence can have one or more words in it. It usually describes an action, and shows what someone or something **does**. A verb or verb phrase can also show what someone or something **is**, and it can show what someone or something **has**.

The ending of a sentence can be called many things. It can be called an object, a description of time, a description of place, a complement, and much more.

Jaymie	is	in the gym.	(subject, verb, description of place)
Jaymie	is throwing	the ball.	(subject, verb, object)
Jaymie	has	a good arm.	(subject, verb, object)

The ending part is not always necessary. In its simplest form, a sentence needs only a **subject** and a **verb** to be complete. For example:

The computer   crashed.
     subject   verb

Exercise A. In the following sentences, underline the subjects, circle the verbs, and put brackets around the endings of each sentence.

Example: Emily loves {ice cream.}

1. Malika babysits her cousins.

2. The table collapsed.

3. The Galleria is in Texas.

4. Jorjia plays paintball.

5. The cowboy saddled his horse.

6. Darryl has a new Discman.

7. Tanya is a great figure skater.

6

Exercise B. Longer sentences can have more than one subject and object. In each example below, two shorter sentences have been joined into one longer sentence by the words "and" and "when". The subjects are underlined, the verbs are in *italics*, and the endings are in brackets.

The <u>baseball</u>   *hit*   {the window,}   and   <u>the glass</u>   *broke*.
    subject   verb   ending/object   subject   verb

The <u>window pane</u>   *broke*   when   <u>the ball</u>   *hit*   {it.}
    subject   verb   subject   verb   ending

In the following sentences, underline the subjects, circle the verbs, and put brackets around the endings of each sentence.

1. The wolf howled at the moon and the campers shivered.

2. I like orange juice, but my sister prefers grape juice.

3. Boots purrs while Buttons chases birds.

4. Andrew likes Andrea, but Andrea likes Albert.

Exercise C. Make up three fun sentences of your own.
For your subjects, use the names of stars from the movies, from television, or from sports.
For your verbs, describe something that the star *does* or *is* or *has*.
For your endings, try to think of an interesting or enjoyable fact or action.
Underline the subjects, circle the verbs (or verb phrases), and put brackets around the endings.

Examples: <u>Jackie Chan</u>   is   {the best kung fu fighter.}
              <u>Angelina Jolie</u>   has   {a very good karate chop.}

1. _____

2. _____

3. _____

Lesson 3 — Nouns and Pronouns

A noun is a specific person, place, or thing.
Pronouns take the place of nouns to make a sentence simpler and smoother.
Sentences which never use pronouns can sound awkward and wordy. For example,

> Harriet lives with Harriet's mother during the week and with Harriet's father on weekends. Harriet's parents both treasure the time Harriet spends with Harriet's mother and father.

Here is the same sentence, but this time it uses pronouns:
> Harriet lives with **her** mother during the week and with **her** father on weekends. Harriet's parents both treasure the time **she** spends with **them**.

Pronouns refer to specific things in a non-specific way. For example, "she" is not specific: "she" could refer to any female. However, since "she" comes after a specific noun, "she" refers to "Harriet". As a general rule, sentences start with a specific noun phrase and subsequently use pronouns to refer to it.

For example: **This <u>sandwich</u>** has too much mustard on **<u>it</u>**.
                          \ noun   \ pronoun

Exercise A. In the following sentences, replace the repeated nouns with pronouns.

1. The trees are beginning to lose the trees' leaves.

_____

2. Tricia can't come to the phone because Tricia is still asleep.

_____

3. Pedro is looking forward to Pedro's day off.

_____

4. The dentist needs to extract Parvati's tooth because the tooth has a cavity.

_____

Exercise B. Rewrite the following sentences replacing the underlined pronouns with possible nouns:

1. My grandmother gave me **<u>it</u>**. _____

2. **<u>He</u>** is going to see a movie tomorrow. _____

3. **<u>You</u>** are my best friend. _____

Lesson 4 — Sentence Fragments

A sentence fragment is a sentence that is missing an important element — the beginning, the verb phrase, or the ending. It's like a Cadillac without an engine: it may look great from the outside, but you can't make it run. Often, a sentence fragment makes no sense at all.

Examples: *Billy is from.* (or)   *Because I like.*

Sometimes, sentence fragments make sense, but they break up the natural flow of a piece of writing, and can be partly confusing. These fragments are acceptable in relaxed conversation, but you would not want to use them in a formal essay for your teacher.

Examples: *The elephant's ballet shoes. Which were pink polka-dotted. And too small.*

A sentence fragment is certainly not *always* a bad thing. It is fine, for example, to use them in conversation:

	(Fragments)
(a) Would you like some pizza?	*Yes.*
(b) Where is the game?	*In the gym.*
(c) Why did you make fun of your little brother?	*Because I felt like it.*

However, if you were to cover up the column of questions and read only the answers, you would be rather confused. What's in the gym? What did you feel like doing?

Exercise A. Put an **X** beside the sentence fragments and a checkmark (✓) beside the complete sentences. Ask yourself: Is any information missing? If so, what is needed to complete the sentence?

1. Angie is my best friend.   ____

2. Because I said so.   ____

3. Never in a million years.   ____

4. Herman likes to.   ____

5. Where the mole people live.   ____

6. He's 13 years old.   ____

7. When I was in Finland.   ____

8. Who was at the party?   ____

9

Exercise B. Rewrite the following paragraph by changing all the sentence fragments into completely finished sentences that make sense:

Aimy took her little brother to. They wanted to buy. Because.
Unfortunately, it was too expensive, so they.   As they were walking.
Then Aimy remembered that she had to.   Kind of funny.
Almost got lost on the way home. Had a couple of milkshakes at home.

_____

_____

_____

_____

_____

_____

_____

_____

_____

_____

_____

Lesson 5 — Sentence Fragments and Conjunctions

Words like "and," "but," and "or" are known as **simple conjunctions**. They form bridges between words and ideas. If a simple conjunction is the first word of a sentence, we often feel as if one end of the bridge is left hanging with nothing to connect to.

Example: *And Marco is going to the party.*

This sentence is incomplete because we don't know who (or what!) is going to be at the party with Marco. This sentence could be very easily corrected if we either added a name at the start or simply removed the "And."

Franco and Marco are going to the party. (or) *Marco is going to the party.*

The following sentence needs a fuller beginning to make sense.

But my Dad wouldn't let me.

To correct it, we can add another sentence:

<u>*I wanted to go on the class trip*</u>, *but my Dad wouldn't let me.*

Exercise A. Turn the following sentence fragments into complete sentences by adding ideas or by getting rid of certain words.

1. But that's beside the point. _____

_____

2. Or the blue dress, I don't care which one. _____

_____

3. And we have to invite Aunt Tilly. _____

_____

4. I like rap. And hip hop. And techno. But I can't stand ska. Or electronica.

_____

_____

5. And don't forget to brush your teeth! _____

_____

6. Or last summer, either. _____

_____

11

Lesson 6 — Stringy Sentences

A sentence fragment stops too soon, or it does not give enough information.
A stringy sentence is the opposite — it just doesn't know when to quit. For example:

> *This weekend I went camping and I was having fun at first but on Saturday night I saw a bear and I thought it looked hungry so I ran away and then I got lost in the woods but then my friend came and found me.*

Some teachers call them "run-on sentences," because they run on and on.
They are like the handkerchief that the clown pulls out of his pocket. A handkerchief is usually no bigger than a table napkin, but this one keeps on coming.

A sentence that keeps on coming like a mile-long string is confusing, and should be broken up into smaller pieces. The sample sentence above could read like this:

> *This weekend I went camping. I was having fun at first. On Saturday night I saw a bear. I thought it looked hungry. I ran away. I got lost in the woods. Then my friend came and found me.*

The problem now is that all the sentences are too short and choppy. They sound as if they are being spoken by a cheap robot.

General Rules for Style:

(a) Use different lengths for your sentences. Some can be short, and some long.

(b) Try not to use the word "and" more than one or two times in a sentence. Two is usually acceptable, but three is definitely a crowd.

(c) The same rule applies to conjunctions such as "but" and "or" — try not to use them more than a couple of times in a sentence.

A final, acceptable correction of the sample sentence on this page could read as follows:

> *This weekend I went camping. I was having fun at first, but on Saturday night I saw a bear. I thought it looked hungry, so I ran away. I got lost in the woods, but then my friend came and found me.*

Exercise A. Rewrite the following stringy sentences by breaking them up into smaller groups of sentences. Avoid choppiness, and use correct punctuation.

1. I asked Molly to go to the movies with me but she said no and then I asked Holly to go to the movies with me but she said she was sick and then I asked Polly to go to the movies with me but she said was moving to Alaska and, in the end, I asked Danika and she said yes.

_____

_____

_____

_____

_____

2. Yesterday I went to the mall and bought a basketball and then I took it over to my friend Shauna's house so that we could shoot some hoops and then I went home and ate supper.

_____

_____

_____

_____

_____

3. I meant to call you Friday night but I couldn't use the phone because my mom was talking to her sister and her sister lives in Japan and then my brother went on-line and refused to get off the Internet.

_____

_____

_____

_____

_____

Lesson 7 — Comma Splices

Another type of stringy sentence is the **comma splice**. This means that two complete sentences have been spliced (joined) together using a comma. For example:

Jamal wants to major in Accounting, it is his favorite subject.

There are several different ways to fix a comma splice. The most common way is to change the comma into a **period** or a **semicolon**.

Jamal wants to major in Accounting. It is his favorite subject. (period)

Or   *Jamal wants to major in Accounting; it is his favorite subject.* (semicolon)

Another way to correct the comma splice is by adding a conjunction, such as "and" or "because". Conjunctions create or clarify a relationship between words or ideas.

*Jamal wants to major in Accounting **because** it is his favorite subject.*

Exercise A. Fill in the blanks using an appropriate conjunction from the list below:

[but, or, and; although (*or* "even though"), so, while, because]

1. There was an electrical storm, _____ the hard drive got fried.

2. I want to be a writer, _____ I've heard there's no money in it.

3. I'll just go to the arcade, _____ you do the groceries.

4. Lea likes to play baseball, _____ she is going to try out for the team.

5. Suzanne said she would put up the decorations for the dance, _____ you'd rather do it.

6. Jimmy pulled the fire alarm, _____ he got a detention.

7. I went fishing with my dad last weekend, _____ it was really cool.

Exercise B. Very simply, re-read all of the comma splice sentences in **Exercise A**, and remember two other ways that are often used to correct them. One is to change the commas to periods, and the other is to change the commas to semicolons. When you do this for sentences 1, 3, 4, 6 and 7, the sentences sound as good as or almost as good as the sentences with the conjunctions added. But sentences 2 and 5 sound much better with the conjunctions.

Do you agree? Can you hear the difference?

Lesson 8 — Parallel Structure

Parallel structure refers to the repetition of certain elements within a single sentence or a whole text. The repeated elements must not be different from each other; they must be in the same grammatical form. If the rhythm or repetition is broken, the sentence is usually incorrect. For example:

✓   We waltz**ed**, we tango**ed**, and we danc**ed** the night away.
✗   We waltz**ed**, we **were tangoing**, and we danc**ed** the night away.

In the first sentence, all the verbs are conjugated in the same tense — the simple past.
In the second sentence, the rhythm is broken in the second verb phrase, which uses the past progressive tense.

In the next example, the three activities all need to be in either the basic form of the word or the form of the word that ends in "-ing".

✗   I love to ski, skate, and snowboarding.
✓   I love skiing, skating, and snowboarding.
✓   I love to ski, to skate and to snowboard. (Also, "I love to ski, skate and snowboard.")

In the following example, the parallel structure works on two levels: the repetition of "if you" and the verb tense. In the second sentence, both parts are changed, and the sentence becomes awkward. The third sentence shows a way to shorten the first sentence, and still keep it parallel.

✓   **If you** **were** older, **if you** **were** more responsible, and **if you** **were** able to listen to reason, then I might have been willing to lend you the car.
✗   **If you** **were** older, **when you** **are** more responsible, and **if you could listen** to reason, I might have been willing to lend you the car.
✓   If you were **older**, **more responsible**, and **able to listen to reason**, then I might have been willing to lend you the car.   [three adjective phrases in a row]

The repetitions in some forms of parallel structures can be a very powerful way to express yourself. A famous example is Martin Luther King Junior's "I have a dream" speech. This speech resonates profoundly not only because of its message, but also because of the powerful repetition of "I have a dream!"

15

Exercise A. Rewrite and correct the following sentences by making them completely parallel.

1. At Gemma's birthday party we swam in her pool, ate tacos, and were watching a movie.

_____

_____

2. Talking about movies is not the same as to talk about TV.

_____

_____

3. Because we all farm the same land, because we all breathe this air, and since we are all drinking the same water, we have a responsibility to protect the environment.

_____

_____

_____

4. In this scene, Carlos will play the Cyclops, Angie is Hera, Natasha will play Io, and Gordon is Zeus.

_____

_____

5. We need to reach out to the people who do not have food, those who are without homes, and the people who do not have hope.

_____

_____

6. My hobbies are snowboarding, playing basketball, and to hang out with my friends.

_____

_____

Lesson 9 — Crossword Puzzle

ACROSS

3. _ _ _ _ _ _ _ _   _ _ _ _ _ _ _ _ _ >> At camp we went horse-back-riding, we roasted marshmallows around a campfire, we slept in a big tent, and we made tea from mint leaves we found in the forest.

6. Tamala bought a bike _ _ _ _ _ _ _ she was tired of walking to school.

7. Whenever you are walking, whenever you are eating, _ _ _ _ _ _ _ _ you are speaking, and whenever you are working, remember to stop and enjoy the beauty of the world around you.

8. "And," "but," and "or" are called _ _ _ _ _ _ _ _ _ _ _.

DOWN

1. _ _ _ _ _ _ _   _ _ _ _ _ _ _ _ >> My mom says I talk too much but I don't think so, it's just that I like to talk and I have a lot to say and so I share it with the world, and everyone listens, most of the time.

2. In #6 ACROSS, "bought" is a verb, "bike" is an object, and "Tamala" is a _ _ _ _ _ _ _.

3. A _ _ _ _ _ _ _ takes the place of a noun to make a sentence simpler.

4. _ _ _ _ _ _ _ _   _ _ _ _ _ _ _ _ >> And Graham.

5. _ _ _ _ _   _ _ _ _ _ _ >> I went swimming yesterday, it was fun.

CLUES: subject; because; parallel structure; conjunctions; stringy sentence; whenever; comma splice; sentence fragment; pronoun

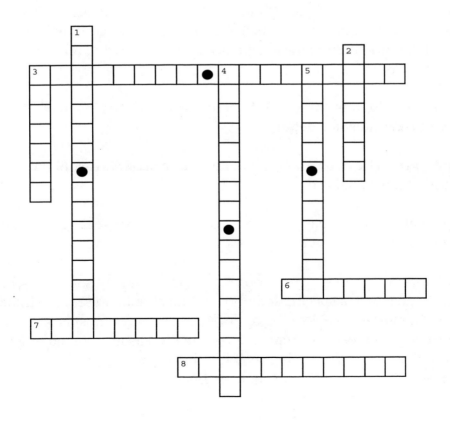

17

Lesson 10 — Composition   *"These are a lot of my favorite things…"*

At the end of this exercise, you will be writing a composition (short essay) that is at least one double-spaced page in length. Your topic will be, "The activities I enjoy the most."

Pre-Writing (keep notes of all your thoughts in the following discussions)

Part 1. In groups right now (or for homework, or brainstorming at your desks), come up with a list of your favorite things to do. Try to name at least five activities.

Part 2. Decide which activity is Number One — which is your single, favorite thing to do.

Part 3. List at least three reasons *why* this activity is your favorite, and add some detail. If you are in a group discussion, listen carefully to the kinds of arguments and details your classmates provide, and make notes. This will help you make your own reasons stronger, clearer, and richer in detail.

Writing, Organization

Here is a suggested outline for your composition.

Introduction. Start by naming all those activities that you love the most. Try to add some detail for each one. Don't just say, "I love to watch TV", but add a phrase such as, "especially MTV while I'm curled up on the couch with a bowl of popcorn on Saturday night." At the end of your first paragraph, state the activity that you love best of all: "However, the thing that I most love to do is…"

Paragraph Two. Use this paragraph to describe *one* of the reasons that you love to do your favorite activity. Add some detail.

Paragraph Three. Use this paragraph to describe a *second* reason that you love to do your favorite activity. Add some detail.

Paragraph Four. Use this paragraph to describe the *main reason*, or the *most important reason* that you love to do your favorite thing.

Conclusion. Wrap your essay up. You could start by saying something like, "Some students might like to do [name a specific activity], and most of them seem to think that [name an activity] is the most enjoyable thing to do, but what I love most is…"
      Next, you can repeat or rephrase your main reasons for enjoying this activity, and you may also wish to add a concluding sentence that begins:
"Nothing beats X…" or "Nothing could be finer than…"

UNIT TWO — QUESTIONS, QUOTATIONS and PRONOUNS

Lesson 11 — Questions?????

There are two main kinds of questions, **"yes/no questions"** and **"information questions"**.

Yes/No questions are questions that can be answered by a simple *yes* or *no*, although these answers can also be added to and clarified with fuller statements.
Most of these questions begin with the following words:

> Did...? Does...? Do...? Was...? Were...? Is...? Are...? Has...? Have...?
> Will...? Can...? Could...? Should...? May...? Might...? Must...?

Examples:

    Q. Did Sammy hit the most home runs last year?
    A. No.
Or,   A. No, he did not.
Or,   A. No, he did not hit the most home runs last year.

    Q. Do rappers have great memories?
    A. Yes, they do.
Or,   A. Yes, most of them have amazing memories.

    Q. Will Shauna go to the movies with us tonight?
    A. No, she has too much homework to do.

Note: The question words *Did, Was,* and *Were* all start questions about the past.
The question words *Do, Were,* and *Have* are almost always followed by the pronoun "you" or by a plural noun or pronoun. Examples: "Do you play ball?" "Have they come home?" "Were the girls at the arcade yesterday?"

Information questions are questions that ask for information about place, time, people, reasons, facts, and manner. Most of these questions begin with the following words:

> Where...? When...? Who...? Whose...? Why...? What...? How...?

The answers can come in short phrases (fragments) or in full sentences. Examples:

    Q. Where did Sammy hit all those home runs?
    A. In Chicago.
Or   A. He hit all those great home runs in Chicago.

    Q. Why does Tawnya watch MTV all the time?
    A. Because she likes music, obviously.
    A. She watches MTV every night because she likes good music, obviously.

Exercise A (oral). Go around the room — each student will ask another student a question, until every student in the class has asked and answered at least one question. The last student will complete the circle by asking a question of the first student. (Another way to do this is for the teacher to ask the first question, and then the last student can ask the teacher a question.) Try to give full sentence answers for each question.

> Example: favorite color
> Question: "What is your favorite color?"
> Answer: "My favorite color is orange."

Things to ask questions about (if you get stuck):

1. Spelling of your name
2. Favorite color
3. Home address
4. Number of brothers
5. Number of sisters
6. Favorite sport
7. Dad's job.
8. Mom's job.
9. Weather
10. Favorite school subject
11. Favorite movie
12. Favorite book
13. Favorite TV show
14. Transportation to school
15. Know a second language?
16. Favorite team, singer, actor, actress

Exercise B. Yes-No Questions
Make up questions that begin with the words in the left margin. Next, supply full-sentence answers for each question, or exchange your list of questions with a partner. You may make up funny questions and crazy answers — just be careful not to upset anyone.

Example: Did...? <u>Did Michael win a gold medal at the Olympics yesterday?</u>
    Answer.   Yes, Michael won a gold medal in the triple jump!

1. Does...? Does_____ ?

Answer: _____

2. Do...? _____ ?

Answer: _____

3. Was...? _____ ?

Answer: _____

4. Were...? _____ ?

Answer: _____

5. Is...? _____ ?

Answer: _____

6. Are...? _____ ?

Answer: _____

7. Has...? _____ ?

Answer: _____

8. Have...? _____ ?

Answer: _____

9. Will...? _____ ?

Answer: _____

10. Can...? _____ ?

Answer: _____

11. Should...?_____ ?

Answer: _____

12. May...? _____ ?

Answer: _____

Exercise C. Information Questions.
Make up questions that begin with the words in the left margin. Next, supply full-sentence answers for each question, or exchange your list of questions with a partner. You may make up funny questions and crazy answers — just be careful not to upset anyone.

Example: What...? <u>What did Michelle do yesterday?</u>
Answer.   Michelle won the statewide mathematics contest!

1. Where...? Where_____ ?

Answer: _____

2. When...? _____ ?

Answer: _____

3. Who...? _____ ?

Answer: _____

4. Whose...? _____ ?

Answer: _____
[Note: "Whose" asks about ownership: "Whose book is that?" Answer: "It's Tami's book."]

5. Why...? _____ ?

Answer: _____

6. What...? _____ ?

Answer: _____

7. How...? _____ ?

Answer: _____

8. How long...? _____ ?

Answer: _____

9. How often...? _____ ?

Answer: _____

Lesson 12 — Tag Questions

A third kind of question is called a "tag question." This is a short question that is added at the end of an affirmative or negative sentence. Forms of the helping verb "Do" are used to start most tag questions:

don't   doesn't   didn't — these negative forms are used at the end of affirmative sentences.

> Jerry **loves** rollerblading, **doesn't** he?
> Moesha's sisters **like** going to concerts, **don't** they?
> The President **learned** how to speak Spanish, **didn't** he?

do   does   did — these positive verbs are used at the end of negative sentences.

> They **do not like** the Vikings very much, **do** they?
> Moesha **doesn't like** going to concerts, **does** she?
> Myles **didn't like** rock and roll when he was a kid, **did** he?

In all other sentences, the first verb in main verb phrase (the helping verb) is the verb used in the tag question. Examples:

> You <u>**will**</u> not [won't] **quit** this job, <u>**will**</u> you?
> Students <u>**should**</u> **drink** more milk, <u>should</u>n't they?

Exercise A. Write the appropriate tag question in the blanks below.

1. You can work tomorrow, _____ ?

2. Mark's sister knows she was adopted, _____ ?

3. These are Trini's earrings, _____ ?

4. Abdul doesn't smoke, _____ ?

5. You're eighteen, _____ ?

6. The Buffalo Bills won't win the Super Bowl, _____ ?

7. Pawcatuck is in Connectictut, _____ ?

8. Tuktoyaktuk is not in Connecticut, _____ ?

9. You have heard of Metallica, _____ ?

10. You wouldn't be able to babysit for me on Saturday, _____ ?

Lesson 13 — Direct Quotations

Whether we are writing or speaking, everything we say is in our own voice.
When we speak in our own voice, it is called "first person" or "first person voice".

When the subject of our sentences is "You", that is called "second person".
Example: *"**You** are so messy, Bubba. Pick up **your** pens and papers right now."*

When the subjects of our sentences can be replaced by the pronouns "He, She, It, They", then we are using what is called the "third person voice".

First person:	I, We.
Second person:	You (singular), You (plural).
Third person:	He, She, It, They

If we express someone else's ideas or words, we must indicate the change of voice in some way. Example: *Bubba said, "I am the neatest person in this room!"*
   In this example, "Bubba" can be replaced by "He" — this is in the third person voice. Then, when Bubba actually speaks, he uses the first person voice ("I am..."), and his words are put into quotation marks.

Quotations can be direct or indirect. A **direct quotation** relates the other person's idea word for word in that person's voice (or the **first person voice**):
   According to Leo Tolstoy, "We can live magnificently in this world if we know how to work and how to love."
   The quotation marks separate the quote from the rest of our text and indicate the introduction of the other person's voice.

An **indirect quotation** relates the other person's idea, but we put it into our own words. We keep the idea, but we alter the words and we continue to use our own **voice**. We do not use quotation marks.
   Leo Tolstoy believed that the ability to love and work well was the key to leading a happy life.

Exercise A. A direct quotation must begin and end with quotation marks. Correct the following sentences by inserting the quotation marks.

1. Rajid shouted, Look out! That truck is coming right for us!

2. My grandmother always says, Count that day lost in which you have learned nothing.

3. If I'd known we were going to the beach, said Joan, I would have brought my swimsuit.

4. One day I'd like to fly an F-22 Raptor, Marjorie said thoughtfully.

5. Does anyone want to go see a movie? Dad asked. I'll pay for it.

6. My guitar lesson isn't until five, Moanda said. We still have an hour.

24

Exercise B. Look carefully at the placement of the commas in **Exercise A**.
Notice how the commas are inserted directly after introductory phrases, just before the quotation begins:

> George shouted, "Watch out for that tree!"
> Mary asked, "You play chess, don't you?"

If the quotation is given at the beginning of the sentence, a comma is placed at the end of the quotation, and then the phrase describing the speaker is added:

> "I'll have some more coffee," Dad said.

If the quotation ends in a question mark or an exclamation mark, do not add a comma.

> "I'll have some more of that great coffee!" Dad exlaimed.
> "When does the party start?" Franco asked.

Finally, the quotations in some sentences start and finish a sentence, and the phrase naming the speaker is placed right in the middle. In this case, usually, use two commas.

> "In the year 2002,"said Mr. Peabody, "will Rocky be able to fly to the moon?"

In the following sentences, put commas in their proper places:

1. Kieran asked "Could you give me some money to rent a video game?"

2. My grandfather always says "If it's worth doing, do it well."

3. "Next Tuesday" said Ms. Garcia "there will be a math test."

4. "I wish we could go to the cottage this weekend" moaned Susie.

5. "Let's order some pizza" said Mike. "I'm starving."

6. "I wonder" Ajani said, looking at the sky "if people will be able to live on Mars one day."

Lesson 14 — Punctuating Direct Quotations

Review

Quotation marks [" "] surround the words that someone else has said or written.
A comma [,] is often used to indicate a pause in a sentence.
In direct quotations, a comma helps indicate the change in voice. For example:

(a) *Consuela asked, "How long will the test be?"*

(b) *"I want a mountain bike for Christmas," said Donald.*
Note: when a comma comes after the quote, it usually goes inside (before) the quotation mark.

(c) *"I have never in my life," claimed Ana, "been so embarrassed."*
Note: when a complete quotation is divided into two parts, a comma goes both after the first part and before the second part to indicate continuation of the thought.

A period [.] comes at the end of a finished, complete statement.
Exclamation marks [!] and question marks [?] come after questions and exclamations, of course!

Exercise A. Fill in the missing punctuation using quotation marks, commas, question marks, and periods.

1.   Uncle Jimmy asked   How old are you now

2.   Let's try out for the band this year   Harley said to Hank

3.   Next summer   Juanita said happily   we're going to Jamaica for a month

4.   I hope you have all enjoyed this evening's presentation   said the emcee

5.   Ho ho ho   chuckled Santa   Merry Christmas

6.   Maxine asked   Could we buy a CD burner

7.   As Juliet puts it   A rose by any other name would smell as sweet

8.   There's something wrong with your funny bone   frowned the doctor

9.   Hey   Mom said   just where do you think you're going

10.   Kareem said   Let's go get an ice cream as soon as the game is over

11.   I promise not to lie this time   the politician said

12.   On the quiz   the teacher informed the class   there will be ten multiple choice questions

Lesson 15 — Indirect Quotations

The main difference between a direct quote and an indirect quote is the voice being heard. When you use a **direct quote**, you are **repeating word for word** what someone else has said. When you use an **indirect quote**, you are paraphrasing what someone else has said; you are putting it into your own words.

Direct quotation.

Alonso said, "It would be impossible for me to attend the party. I have many tasks to complete in the next few days."

Indirect quotation.

Alonso explained that he couldn't go to the party because he had a lot of work to do.

Knowing how to paraphrase is an essential skill, especially for writing research reports and essays. It's a skill that you probably already have without realizing it. When you repeat a joke, do you recite it word for word? Or do you simply remember its essence, its main idea, and put that into your own words?

Exercise A. Change the following direct quotations to indirect quotations by paraphrasing their content. *(Relax, and be creative with this one — there are no precise answers. Although it may seem quite hard at first to imagine a different way to express the idea, there are ways to make it easier. Cover the words with your hand, then try to remember it. Or tell a friend about the idea. Remember, it's just like retelling a joke.)*

1. "Don't be afraid," Tallulah whispered to Kay. "All the bears are hibernating at this time of year."

   _____

   _____

2. My neighbor looked at me and said, "With all the awful things happening right now, I figure this world is going to Hades in a handbasket."

   _____

   _____

3. "I despise the excruciating time lapse," said Mr. Dutell, "between the moment I click my mouse and the time it takes my screen to fully load."

   _____

   _____

Lesson 16 — Apostrophes to Show Ownership, Possession

Apostrophes are often used to show ownership.
Instead of saying, *"Jessica owns that camera,"* we can say, *"That is Jessica's camera."*

If the word already has an "s" at the end, there is usually no need to add another "s".
Those are my neighbors' trees.   That is James' camera.

If both Jessica and James own the same camera, the apostrophe goes after the second person's name: *That is James and Jessica's camera.*

If Jessica and James each own a different camera, the apostrophe goes after both names:
Those are Jessica's and James' cameras.

{This sentence is a bit awkward, however. It would be better to say,
Those cameras belong to Jessica and James.}

Exercise A. Rewrite the following sentences to show ownership using apostrophes.

Example: Change *"I love the TV belonging to my sister."* to *"I love my sister's TV."*

1. That fence belongs to my neighbors. _____

   _____

2. Harvey owns that guitar. _____

3. One cat belongs to Martha and the other cat belongs to Larry. _____

   _____

4. My mother and father own this store. _____

   _____

5. Would you like to go swimming in the pool that belongs to my grandparents?

   _____

   _____

6. Have you tried the recipe invented by Billy for Texas-style BBQ sauce?

   _____

7. The green station wagon belongs to my uncle and the red convertible belongs to my aunt.

_____

_____

8. The accounts of this business need to be reorganized. _____

_____

Exercise B. Rephrase the following sentences so that they accurately show ownership *without* using apostrophes.

Example: Change *"Have you seen Mary's hat?"* to *"Have you seen a hat belonging to Mary?"*

1. Welcome to Gary and Harry's amusement park.

_____

2. Those are Polly's and Esther's pants. _____

_____

3. Why are Franklin's cat and Shania's cat so cute? _____

_____

Exercise C. Every student in the class should donate an object to a pile in the middle of the room. These objects can be pencil cases, shoes, hats, and so on. The teacher will hold up each object in turn, and ask a student to make up two sentences indicating ownership. At least one of the two sentences should use the apostrophe form.

Example: *That is Billy's hat.* {and} *That hat belongs to Billy.* {or} *Billy is the owner of that hat.*

When the sentences are completed, the student owning the object will get the object back.

Lesson 17 — Possessive Pronouns

Apostrophes are used with **nouns** to indicate possession:
   ✓   That is Bill and Jessie**'s** house. This is my mother**'s** favorite book.

Pronouns, however, **do not** use apostrophes to indicate possession:
   ✗   That house is **their's**.   ✗   This book is **her's**.

Possessive pronouns look like this:
   ✓   That house is **theirs**.   This book is **hers**.
   ✓   That is **their** house.   This is **her** book.

Exercise A. Fill in the blanks using the appropriate possessive pronoun.
{my, mine, your, yours, his, her, hers, its, our, ours, their, theirs}

1. Raise _____ hand if you have any questions.

2. We are planning to take _____ vacation in August.

3. Wanda claims that those gloves are not _____.

4. Did anyone see where I put _____ glasses?

5. You have to return that book to the library! It isn't _____ to keep!

6. I thought these footballs belonged to Ollie and Mo, but they say those ones aren't

_____.

7. Kayla and _____ friends went to Rome last February.

8. I'm searching for a certain pen of _____ that I misplaced.

9. My dad promised to lend me _____ lucky socks for the tournament.

10. No matter what the stewardess says, my family and I are positive that this luggage is

_____.

Exercise B. In the blanks, replace the underlined possessive noun with the appropriate possessive pronoun.

1. Niles is not answering <u>Niles'</u> phone. _____

2. Fatima and Aisha are very proud of <u>Fatima and Aisha's</u> prize-winning essay. _____

3. Louella hopes that one day the family business will be <u>Louella's</u>. _____

4. Thomas and Trina tried to convince me that the fireworks weren't <u>Thomas and Trina's</u>,

but I knew better. _____

Lesson 18 — It's and Its

The word "it" is a pronoun. When "it" is used to show possession, it does not use an apostrophe.

   ✓   "The <u>monster's</u> claws were slimy." — is correct,

   ✗   "<u>It's</u> claws were slimy." — is incorrect.

   ✓   "<u>Its</u> claws were slimy." — is correct

This may seem confusing at first, but there's a very easy way to remember this rule: **the term "it's" *always* means "it is."** Whenever you're unsure whether to write "it's" or "its," read the sentence back to yourself. For example, "It is claws were slimy" does not make any sense! *(This trick is also very helpful whenever you need to remember the difference between "you're" and "your," or "they're" and "their" — "you're" always means "you are," and "they're" always means "they are"!)*

Exercise A. Put a ✓ beside the sentences that use "it's" and "its" correctly, and an ✗ beside the sentences that are incorrect.

___ 1.   A spider monkey can swing from tree to tree with its tail.

___ 2.   Jamie's dog doesn't like it when you touch it's ears.

___ 3.   Each new day is its own adventure.

___ 4.   My grandfather's knee tells him when it's going to rain.

___ 5.   Its my birthday today!

___ 6.   My video game controller is missing it's buttons.

___ 7.   It's time for the movie to start.

___ 8.   Sometimes a lion will eat it's own children.

___ 9.   When the bell rings, its time to go.

___ 10.   I always laugh when I see my cat chasing it's tail!

___ 11.   Let me show you how its done.

___ 12.   The journey is its own reward.

Exercise B. Write one sentence using "it's", and a second sentence using "its."

1. _____

_____

2. _____

_____

31

Lesson 19 — Crossword Puzzle

ACROSS.   Fill in the blanks, and add each word to the crossword puzzle:

2. "A quotation using the actual words of a speaker is a _ _ _ _ _ _ quotation," said the teacher.

6. "Your," "its," and "their" are examples of _ _ _ _ _ _ _ _ _ _ _ _ _ _ _ _ _ _.

7. The teacher informed the class that a quotation which alters (or paraphrases) the words of a speaker is called

_ _ _ _ _ _ _ _.

8. A noun uses an _ _ _ _ _ _ _ _ _ _ to indicate possession; personal pronouns do not.

DOWN.   Fill in the blanks, and add each word to the crossword puzzle:

1. "Are you tired?" is a _ _ _ / _ _ type of question.

3. The last part of this question — "You know Dikembe, don't you?" — is called a

_ _ _ _ _ _ _ _ _ _ _.

4. "What are your hobbies?" is an _ _ _ _ _ _ _ _ _ _ type of question.

5. These symbols — " " — are called _ _ _ _ _ _ _ _ _ _ _ _ _ _.

32

Lesson 20 — Composition *"Good Questions; Good Answers"*

Pre-Writing

What are the questions that you would most like answers to? In groups, talk about the questions that students in your group would like to have answers to. Write at least four of these questions out on a piece of paper.

Next, go through each question, and see if anyone in the group has answers. Take notes during the discussion, writing down any good new questions that come to mind. You do not *have to* use any or all of the group's questions for your own composition.

Writing the Composition

After the discussion, return to your desks and write a composition of approximately two double-spaced pages. You may use the following outline if you wish.

Introduction: There are many questions that students in today's world would like to know the answers for. Some of these questions are:

1. _____

2. _____

3. _____

4. _____

The question I would like to answer is number 1 (or 2, or 3…), because
(*it's the most fun,* or *it's the only one I know anything about,* or *it's the most important.*)

Your question can be a light one or a serious one: "Why is So-and-So such a great entertainer?" or "Why is there so much pain in the world?" Choose two or three reasons for your answer, and make each one of those reasons the basis for the next three paragraphs.

Paragraph Two. "So-and-So is a great entertainer because she is a fabulous dancer." Give examples; explain what you mean by this.

Paragraph Three. "Because she is an extremely funny person." Examples, explanations.

Paragraph Four. "Because she sings songs that mean something." Examples, explanations.

Conclusion. Round off your composition by rephrasing your main points, but with a fresh perspective. Don't simply repeat yourself. Try hard to convince your readers!

UNIT THREE — COMMANDS and DICTION

Lesson 21 — Commands

"Don't go there!" "Pass the ball to me." "Watch this!" Sentences like this can be called different things: imperatives, commands or orders. These sentences can be spoken in anger, or as warnings, or as helpful instructions or advice.

Anger   "*Get away from my car!*"
Warning   "*Turn your back on that guy — he'll kill you!*"
Direction   "*Go five miles down Laker Avenue, and turn right on Sun Street.*"
Advice   "*Take two headache pills and drink a glass of hot cocoa.*"
Order   "*Start your grammar engines, ladies and gentlemen, and do the following exercises!*"

Notice that commands usually begin with the plain form of a verb. The subject of the sentence is "You", but this is usually unspoken. Sometimes we add a "You" to the start of the command, but we will add a pause after the "You", or we will start the sentence with the phrase, "Hey, you" or "You there":
        "*Hey you — get away from my car!*"
Also, sometimes we add the name of the person to the beginning of a command:
        "*Mom, tell Joe to stop bugging me.*"

Exercise A. Practice writing commands:

1. Give the first couple of **directions** explaining how to get to your house from school:

_____

_____

2. In an **angry** voice, command a stranger to do something: _____

_____

3. **Order** your parents to do something: _____

_____

4. Give **advice** to a friend on how to do well on a test: _____

_____

5. Give a **warning** to a pesky little brother, sister, or cousin: _____

_____

Lesson 22 — Changing Direct Commands into Indirect Commands

There are two main ways to change direct quotations of commands to indirect quotations of commands. For example:

Tawnya said, "Buy your own calculator, Billy!"

The first way is shown in the following example:

Tawnya told Billy __to__ buy his own calculator.

The second is to use the linking word **"that"** and additional verbs such as "should", "ought to", "had to" or "needed to":

Tawnya told Billy __that he should__ buy his own calculator.
Tawnya told Billy __that he ought to__ buy his own calculator.
Tawnya told Billy __that he had to__ buy his own calculator.
Tawnya told Billy __that he needed to__ buy his own calculator.

Exercise A: Using *to, ought to, had to, needed to*, and *should*, change the following direct commands into indirect commands:

1. The sergeant commanded his troops, "Drop and give me fifty push-ups!"_____

_____

2. Marco yelled, "Pat, watch out for that guy — he has a gun!"_____

_____

3. Benny said, "Just drink some soda, Crystal, and your stomach ache will go away."

_____

_____

4. The hippie said to the officer, "Make love, not war."_____

_____

5. Mr. Chu shouted, "Hey kid, get down from that tree!"_____

_____

6. Ursuline teased her older brother, "Take mom to the prom with you!"_____

_____

7. Mrs. Jetson told her daughter, "Buy some nice clothes with your birthday money."

_____

Lesson 23 — Changing Indirect Commands into Direct Commands

There are a number of ways to change indirect commands into direct commands. For example:

>Tawnya told Billy <u>that he needed to</u> buy his own calculator.

Could become: *Tawnya said, "Billy, buy your own calculator!"*

Or: *"Buy your own calculator!" Tawnya told Billy.*

We saw in the last exercise that expressions such as *"that he needed to"* are often added to a paraphrased command. This means that the speaker's original statement has been changed. In the following exercise, you need to imagine what the speaker's original words were, and then put them inside quotation marks.

    Whether you place the quotation first and name the speaker afterward — or the speaker first and the quotation afterward — is up to you. Go with your gut feeling — which sounds better?

Exercise A. Change the indirect quotations into direct quotations.

1. The fireman instructed the children to stop, drop, and roll if they ever caught on fire.

_____

_____

2. Mrs. Li reminded her son that he needed to buy a present for his father's birthday.

_____

_____

3. The card Rochelle had picked up told her to not pass "GO."

_____

_____

4. Tyrell instructed the lost child to walk down Third Street and turn right on Blair.

_____

_____

5. Kassandra yelled that somebody should call the police. _____

_____

6. Jocko's parents ordered him to go to his room and think about what he'd done.

_____

_____

7. Hailey told her friends to bring soda pop, chips, and candy to the picnic. _____

_____

_____

8. Salem told his brother that if he wanted to avoid fighting, he had to stay calm, ignore

insults, and walk away. _____

_____

_____

Lesson 24 — Changing Angry Commands into Polite Questions

Some commands are **polite**:
  "Go up highway 9 and take the Glavistock Road exit."

Others are **not polite**:
  "Get your filthy hands off my purse!"

This type of command can be expressed in a more polite way if it is expressed as a question:
  "Would you \
          please remove your hands from my purse?"
  "Could you /

Exercise A. Translate the following commands into polite questions.

1. "Hey, you kids — get off my property!"_____

_____

2. "Mom, buy me a mountain bike!"_____

_____

37

3. "Get your smelly mutt away from my purebred poodle!"_____

_____

4. "Young man, you march right on up to your room this instant!"_____

_____

5. "Slow this car down before we hit something!"_____

_____

6. "Stop picking your nose in public!"_____

_____

7. "Say something more interesting!"_____

_____

8. "Pick up the dang phone already!"_____

_____

9. "Just eat the stupid meatloaf before I shove it down your throat!"_____

_____

10. "Leave me alone!"_____

_____

11. "Fluffy, stop twinkling on the neighbor's lawn!"_____

_____

Lesson 25 — Shortening Words (Contractions)

When we speak, we often squeeze words together. "I would" becomes "I'd," "will not" becomes "won't," and so on. When you collapse two words into one, it's called a *contraction*. When something *contracts*, it gets smaller.

In formal writing — for example, in school essays — you should use the longer versions of words. You don't have to do this when you're writing informally (in short stories, for example, or in letters to friends).

In contractions, a single apostrophe is used to replace the missing part of a word. For example:

      (a) *You <u>have</u> been to Iowa.* → *You've been to Iowa.*
      (b) *Romeo <u>is</u> in Verona.* → *Romeo's in Verona.*
      (c) *Where <u>did</u> you go?* → *Where'd you go?*

Exercise A. Underline or highlight the contractions (five of them) in the first two paragraphs above, the ones that begins with the words, "When we speak…").

Exercise B. Replace the words in brackets with contractions.

1. Shaun *(does not)* _____ want to try out for soccer this year.

2. *(They are)* _____ under a lot of stress right now.

3. My parents *(would not)* _____ let me go to the concert.

4. *(It is)* _____ a beautiful day.

5. *(Have not)* _____ you ever seen purple hair before?

6. *(Do not)* _____ go there.

7. Alex *(will not)* _____ be able to drive for 3 more years.

8. *(You have)* _____ got to be kidding!

9. *(Let us)* _____ go to the mall after school.

10. *(That is)* _____ a wrap!

Lesson 26 — Slang Vocabulary

Language has many levels. There are the words that you use when you're "hanging out" with your friends, and then there are the words that you use in front of your grandmother, grandfather, pastor, priest, imam, rabbi, teacher, or boss.

No one level of language is always better than another one — each one has its own appropriate time and place.

Compare: *"Great idea, Mr. Trump!"*
with: *"That idea, like, totally rocks, boss-man."*

Or: *"Don't go there, girlfriend."*
with: *"That topic is not open for discussion, my friend."*

Exercise A. Rewrite the following terms in formal language.

1. Chill out _____

2. Cop _____

3. Whassup? _____

4. Ain't _____

5. Dude _____

6. Babe _____

7. Bummer _____

8. That sucks _____

9. Phat _____

10. Let's split _____

Exercise B. Part of the interest and the beauty of slang is that it is always changing. Words go in and out of fashion more quickly than clothing styles do. In fact, there were probably a number of terms in **Exercise A** that were out of date, and made you laugh.

This is why a formal level of language is useful — since it stays fairly constant from year to year, it allows people to communicate clearly without worrying that a certain word or expression is outdated.

Rewrite the following terms using current slang words:

1. Very good _____

2. Attractive person _____

3. Friend _____

4. That's unfortunate _____

4. Strange _____

Lesson 27 — Slang Syntax

While certain forms of English are considered "correct" and others "incorrect," it may interest you to know that the English language, for a brief time in its long history, was once considered to be a language only spoken by the lower classes. Modern English developed as a slangy dialect mixing French with a native Teutonic dialect (known as "Englisc") after the Normans conquered Britain in the 11th century.

The main difference between slang and "formal" or "proper" speech is largely a question of numbers — as the number of people speaking a particular dialect or using a particular phrase increases, the more acceptable that language becomes. This may seem unfair, but it does make sense. The purpose of language is to communicate — to understand and to be understood. In order for us to understand each other, we need to have common words and common rules of speech. This group of rules, the way we put words together to form a grammatically correct sentence, is called **syntax**.

A second reason that some language is considered slang, even if many people use it, is that people tend to agree on the following distinction. They feel that certain kinds of language are appropriate for relaxed conversation in the street, and that other kinds of language are appropriate in formal settings, as in the writing of careful, complex essays to be read by our peers, parents, and teachers. The most obvious form of slang is *swearing*. We may hear it all the time, but we do not use it in our formal speech and writing in the classroom.

Exercise A. The following sentences are incorrect for classroom use (even though they may sound just fine for relaxed speech). Rewrite them in formal English.

1. Where you at? _____

2. He my best friend. _____

3. I is happy because I be goin' to Japan for a month. _____

_____

4. Whatcha up to this weekend? _____

5. Didja go catch a movie? _____

6. I be chillin' out. _____

7. Aintcha comin'? _____

8. This be my first day off in a month, so I's gonna enjoy it. _____

_____

9. She done ate my French fries. _____

10. I ain't gonna argue with you, because you is too stubborn. _____

_____

11. If you cain't say anything nice, keep your trap shut. _____

_____

12. Who there? _____

13. Clarissa my mother's cousin. _____

14. You all bust my window! _____

15. You the man. _____

Exercise B. Write out four expressions or sentences that you think are slang. Below each one, write a corrected version — one that you think would be good enough for a composition.

Example: (a) Jerry ripped me off when I bought that CD player from him.
             (b) Jerry charged me too much money for that CD player.

1(a) [slang] _____

1(b) [formal] _____

2(a) [slang] _____

2(b) [formal] _____

3(a) [slang] _____

3(b) [formal] _____

4(a) [slang] _____

4(b) [formal] _____

Lesson 28 — Slang and Direct Quotations

One very common form of slang is to speak of the past in the present tense.

For example,   *"I **went biking** with Chet and we **saw** a bear."*

becomes: *"So **I'm biking** with Chet, right, and we **see** this bear..."*

Another common change is to replace "said" with "goes," "is like," or "is all."

For example,   *Chet says, "Do you want to go biking?"*

becomes: *Chet goes, "Do you wanna go biking?"*
or   *Chet's like, "Do you wanna go biking?"*
or   *Chet's all, "Do you wanna go biking?"*

As an indirect quotation — in proper, formal English — this could become:

Chet asked if I wanted to go biking.

Exercise A. Write down three slangy sentences that use direct quotations, similar to the ones in the examples above. Perhaps you don't need to do anything more than remember things that you or your friends said to each other in the past 24 hours.

Next, rewrite each sentence, but do three things:
(1) Change the slangy language into formal English.
(2) Change the present tense to the past tense.
(3) Paraphrase the direct quotations into indirect quotations.

Example: (a) Miguel goes to me, "This is a great burger, dude."
        (b) Miguel told me that his hamburger was very good.

1(a) [slang] _____

1(b) [formal] _____

2(a) [slang] _____

2(b) [formal] _____

3(a) [slang] _____

3(b) [formal] _____

44

Lesson 29 — More Fun with Slang

Exercise A.   Rewrite the following paragraph,
(1) changing the slangy language into formal English,
(2) changing the present tense to the past tense, and
(3) paraphrasing the direct quotations into indirect quotations.

So, Patti and I went to catch some rays at the beach last Saturday. As we're laying out our towels, I notice this guy riding the waves. I'm like, "Check out that totally hot surfer dude! I'm gonna go hit on him!" And Patti's like, "You go, girl!" So he comes out of the water, right, and I walk up to him and I go "Hey, baby, your daddy's a thief." And he goes, "Huh?" And I'm all, "Cause he stole the stars from the skies and put them in your eyes." And he's like, "That line is more stale than your breath, girl, go get some gum!" I couldn't believe he totally dissed me!

_____

_____

_____

_____

_____

_____

_____

_____

_____

Lesson 30 — Composition *"Giving Instructions"*

In class, or as homework…

Choose a topic from the list below, and write out a series of instructions. You should be able to finish your instructions in about half a page of writing.

Next, be prepared to read your instructions to the rest of the class. The teacher may choose five or six people from the class, or he/she may decide to put you into small groups, so that all students have a chance to read their compositions.

Try to be as clear as you possibly can. At the end of your reading, ask if anyone was unclear about the instructions or about the language that you used, and ask how you could have made your instructions even better.

1. Teach someone how to play your favorite video game. Use at least **five sentences** which give commands. Also, use words such as "first," "second," "third" or "next" and "then" to help show the different stages in the instructions.

2. Give someone directions to your favorite store or shopping mall. Make sure there are at least **five changes of direction**. If your favorite mall or store is right next to your house, then give directions to a different place.

3. Give advice to a younger brother or sister (or a friend who is younger than you are) who is coming into Grade 6 (or 7, 8, or 9) for the first time. If you are in Grade 7, for example, give advice about going to Grade 6 for the first time. If you are in Grade 9, give advice about going to Grade 8 (and so on). Tell your reader what kind of clothes to wear, how to behave, who to be careful about, which school rules to pay attention to, what language to avoid, and any other advice you think is important.

4. Give advice on how to be a fun babysitter. You can follow a chronological order, starting with the best thing to do when you arrive, and finishing with the last fun thing you do before you leave the house. Include at least **five actions**: they can be fun things that you do, but they can also be actions that you need to take to keep the children in line.

5. Tell your listeners how to make your favorite food. Make sure there are at least **five steps** in this process. (Don't just say, "I take the pizza pockets out of the wrapper, and then I put them in the microwave for two minutes.")

UNIT FOUR — PRESENT TIME

Verbs are probably the hardest part of English grammar, because they are so important in every sentence, and because each verb can be put into many different forms. Verbs can be used to describe the past, the present time, and the future.

Last year: I *was* a football star. You *were* my agent. She *was* my coach.
             I *ran* to the endzone. You *screamed*. My coach *jumped* for joy.

This year: I *am* a football star. You *are* my agent. She *is* my coach.
             I *run* to the endzone. You *scream*. My coach *jumps* for joy.

Next year: I *will be* a football star. You *will be* my agent. She *will be* my coach.
             I *will run* to the endzone. You *will scream*. My coach *will jump* for joy.

In this Unit, we are going to emphasize the different kinds of verbs that describe the **present** time.

Three Tenses in the Present Time: Simple Present, Present Progressive, Present Perfect.

Simple Present. In its simplest form, a verb is known as "the simple present." Sometimes, the simple present really is simple. We use it to describe something that is true at the present time. Example: *"I am in this classroom."* Or, *"I see Kobe Bryant -- he is right there!"*

However, the simple present tense can be more complicated than that. It is often used to describe something that was true in the past, is still true, and will probably be true for at least part of the future. Example: *"You are a football star."* This means that you were a star last year, probably, and maybe even for the past 5 or 10 years. It also means that you are a star at the present moment — and you will probably be a star for at least a little while into the future.

Here is another example of a simple present verb that describes past, present and future: "Flowers are beautiful." This sentence actually uses the verb to mean that the statement is "timeless", or always true — the speaker believes it is true from the beginning of time to the end of time.

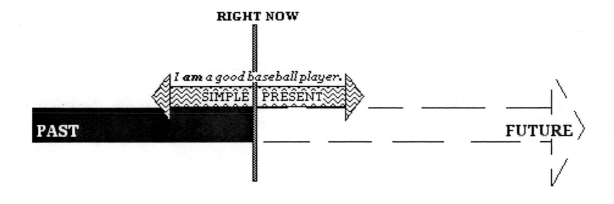

47

Present Progressive. Verbs can also be part of phrases that emphasize an action that is in progress at the present moment. Something "is happening" or "is taking place" right now. Verb phrases that emphasize what is occurring right now are called "present progressive".

They usually have two parts, a form of the verb "BE" in the first part, and the "-ING" form of the main verb. This "-ING" form of the verb is also called the "PRESENT PARTICIPLE".

Subject/Beginning   Verb = Two Parts.

                           1. BE   2. Main Verb & -ing

I   am   playing.   (play & -ing)
You   are   playing.
He/She/It   is   playing.
They   are   playing.

More examples of the present progressive verb tense:

"I am speaking." "You are calling people." "She is directing the movie."
"I am running to the endzone." "You are screaming." "My coach is jumping for joy."

Each of these verb phrases describes an event that began sometime in the past, and will probably continue for at least a short time into the future, but the main emphasis is on the action that is happening right now.

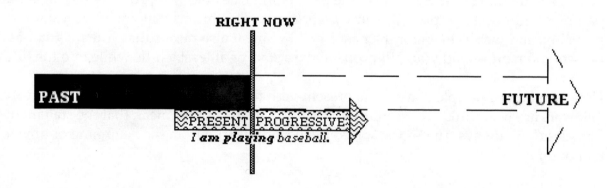

[Note: we use wavy lines in all of our graphs depicting progressive verbs. The waves are supposed to show that these verb phrases emphasize an action or situation that is in progress.]

Present Perfect. Verb phrases that are called "present perfect" describe a time period that begins in the past and moves right up to the present time. They often **emphasize** an action that started in the recent past and has recently been completed:

  *"I **have** (just) **eaten** my lunch."*

The word "perfect" for this tense is a bit confusing, because most of us think "perfect" means something like getting a perfect score on a test, or having "a perfect day." There is an older meaning of "perfect," though, and that meaning is very similar to "finished" or "completed."

Specifically, the present perfect tense usually describes an action that began in the past, and has recently been completed, or that is still true right up until the present moment.

   Example: *"I have been a teacher for two years."*

This describes a process that began two years ago, and is true right up until the present time.

The present perfect is composed of the helping verb "HAVE" and the Past Participle form of the main verb. This past participle is often in the same form as the simple past form of the verb.

*He **tried** to win the championship last year.* (simple past form; single event in the past)

*For seven years now, he **has tried** to win the championship.* (present perfect form;
   "HAS" plus "past participle"; seven years ago, up till present time)

*Since I was a child, I **have played** a lot of baseball.*
   (began in past; has continued until the present time)

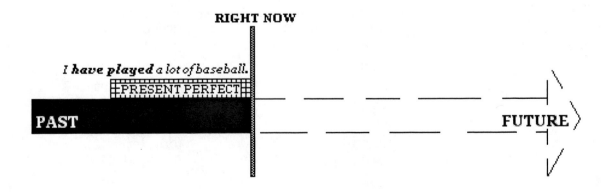

49

For many verbs, however, there is a difference between the form for the **simple past** and the form for the **past participle**.

See the following chart for "Commonly Used Irregular Verbs", and remember that the following "Past Participles" are preceded by "have" or "has" in the present perfect tense.

CHART: COMMON IRREGULAR VERBS

Base form	Simple Past form	Past Participle
awake	awoke	*(has, have)* awakened
be (is, are)	was, were	been
bear [to give birth]	bore	borne, born
become	became	become
begin	began	begun
bend	bent	bent
bet	bet	bet
bite	bit	bitten
blow	blew	blown
break	broke	broken
bring	brought	brought
build	built	built
burst	burst	burst
catch	caught	caught
choose	chose	chosen
come	came	come
cost	cost	cost
cut	cut	cut
deal	dealt	dealt
dig	dug	dug
dive	dove, dived	dived
do	did	done
drag	dragged	dragged
draw	drew	drawn
dream	dreamed, dreamt	dreamed, dreamt
drink	drank	drunk
drive	drove	driven
eat	ate	eaten
fall	fell	fallen
feel	felt	felt
find	found	found
fit	fit, fitted	fit, fitted
fly	flew	flown
forbid	forbad, forbade	forbidden
forget	forgot	forgotten, forgot
freeze	froze	frozen

Base form	Simple Past form	Past Participle
get	got	got, gotten
give	gave	given
go	went	gone
grow	grew	grown
hang [to suspend]	hung	hung
hang [to execute]	hanged	hanged
hear	heard	heard
hit	hit	hit
hurt	hurt	hurt
know	knew	known
lead	led	led
lend	lent	lent
let	let	let
lie [to recline]	lay	lain
light	lit, lighted	lit, lighted
lose	lost	lost
pay	paid	paid
put	put	put
ride	rode	ridden
ring	rang	rung
rise	rose	risen
run	ran	run
say	said	said
see	saw	seen
set [to place]	set	set
shake	shook	shaken
shine	shone, shined	shone, shined
shrink	shrank	shrunk
shut	shut	shut
sing	sang	sung
sink	sank	sunk
sit [to sit down]	sat	sat
slay	slew	slain
speak	spoke	spoken
split	split	split
spread	spread	spread
spring	sprang	sprung
steal	stole	stolen
strike	struck	struck, stricken
swear	swore	sworn
swim	swam	swum
take	took	taken

Lesson 31 — Simple Present; Present Progressive; Present Perfect

Exercise A. Underline the verb or verb phrases in the following sentences, and identify their types in the blanks on the right side of the page.
For the simple present tense, write "Simple."
For the present progressive tense, write "Progressive."
For the present perfect tense, write "Perfect."

Georgia has played a lot of basketball.   Perfect .
Georgia plays basketball every day.   Simple .
Georgia is playing a game right now.   Progressive .

1. Fred and Mike are playing video games.   _____

2. Ella-Mae has played a lot of sports over the years.   _____

3. I am hungry.   _____

4. Sheila is shopping for shoes.   _____

5. Yolanda has danced in professional jazz troupes.   _____

6. Paul is reading quietly under a tree.   _____

7. You have completed the exercise — almost!   _____

8. Timmy goes to daycare while his mother works.   _____
   [two separate verbs; both are the same type]

9. Most sunsets over the ocean are beautiful.   _____

Lesson 32 — Simple Present and Expressions of Frequency

Simple present tense.

Sometimes, the simple present really is simple. We use it to describe something that is true at the present time.

Examples: *"I **am** a member of N'Sync."* Or, *"I **see** Jennifer Lopez — she **is** right there!"*

However, the simple present tense can be more complicated than that. It is often used to describe something that was true in the past, is still true, and will probably be true for at least part of the future. Example: *"You are a good singer."* This means that you were a good singer last year, probably, and maybe even for the past 5 or 10 years. It also means that you are a good singer at the present moment — and you will probably be a good singer for at least a little while into the future.

Here is another example of a simple present verb that describes past, present and future: *"Chocolate bars **are** great."* This sentence actually uses the verb to mean that the statement is "timeless", or always true — the speaker believes it is true from the beginning of time to the end of time.

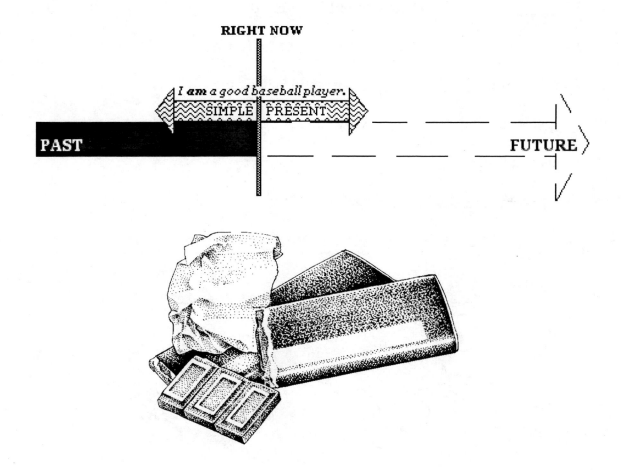

Exercise A. Fill in the blanks in the following sentences with a verb conjugated in the **simple present**.

1. Harvey always _____ the bus to school.

2. You never _____ to me!

3. Nestor and Maxine _____ brother and sister.

4. My parents usually _____ out of town on the weekends.

5. I _____ the color pink.

6. Treena rarely _____ in her pool.

7. Rusty _____ his dog every day.

8. A teacher _____ a lot of tests in a year.

9. We _____ chess or checkers every day.

10. I sometimes _____ a hamburger for lunch.

11. Jesse frequently _____ questions in class.

12. My pet rock _____ very cute.

13. Denis and Darla _____ how to tango.

14. This psychic _____ palms.

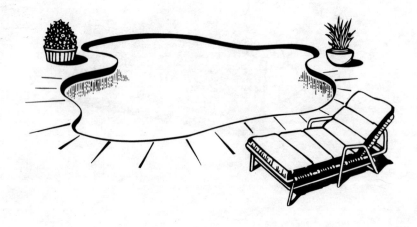

Exercise B. While completing **Exercise A**, you may have noticed that words such as "always," "usually," "sometimes," "rarely," and "never" often accompany verbs conjugated in the simple present. These adverbial expressions describe the *frequency* of the action being discussed.

In the blanks below, write in the **expression of frequency** that accurately describes *your life* or *your opinion*.

always
usually   frequently   often
sometimes   occasionally   now and again   now and then
seldom   infrequently   rarely   hardly ever
never

1. I am _____ late for class.

2. My friends and I _____ talk on the phone.

3. On the weekends, I _____ stay up past midnight.

4. I _____ wear black clothing.

5. Television is _____ entertaining.

6. I _____ wake up at six in the morning or earlier.

7. My family _____ eats supper together.

8. Astrological information is _____ accurate.

9. I use computers _____.

10. Gym class is _____ fun.

TAURUS

55

Lesson 33 — Present Progressive

Verbs can also be part of phrases that emphasize an action that is in progress at the present moment. Something "is happening" or "is taking place" right now. Verb phrases that emphasize what is occurring right now are called "present progressive".

They usually have two parts, a form of the verb "BE" in the first part, and the "-ING" form of the main verb. This "-ING" form of the verb is also called the "PRESENT PARTICIPLE".

Subject/Beginning   Verb = Two Parts.

                           1. BE   2. Main Verb & -ing

I   am   acting.   (act & -ing)
You   are   acting.
He/She/It   is   acting.
They   are   acting.

More examples of the present progressive verb tense:

"I am dancing." "You are spinning the records." "She is directing the video."
"I am running for the exit." "You are all screaming." "My fans are jumping for joy."

Each of these verb phrases describes an event that began sometime in the past, and will probably continue for at least a short time into the future, but the main emphasis is on the action that is **happening right now**.

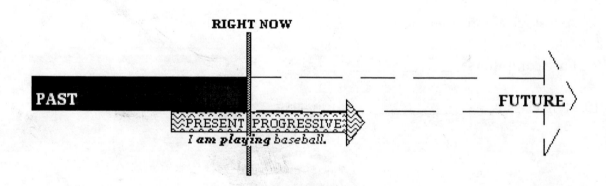

56

Exercise A. One of the best ways to understand the progressive aspect of a verb is to describe someone who is performing an action.

First, the teacher will command a student to do something. Next, the teacher will ask another student to describe what that student is doing (using the present progressive).

Teacher: "Danielle, jump up and down… Manuel, tell us what Danielle is doing."
Manuel: "Danielle is jumping up and down."

1. Sit down slowly.
2. Do a little dance.
3. Look out the window.
4. Celebrate a goal.
5. Stare at your feet.
6. Cheer as if you're at a concert.
7. Flex your biceps.
8. Rap your knuckles on the desk.
9. Scratch your head.
10. Play a bit of air guitar.
11. Repeat a kung fu action.
12. Pretend you're eating an ice cream cone.
13. Hum or whistle something
14. Make a funny face.

Exercise B. Simple Present and Present Progressive

Fill in the blanks with the appropriate form of the verb in parentheses.
Use the Simple Present tense or the Present Progressive tense.

1. Tyrone (be) _____ a very good break dancer. There he is right now! He (dance)

_____ in front of Jackie and Denise.

2. Terry (love) _____ chocolate chip cookies. He (sit)

_____ in the cafeteria right about now, and he (eat)

_____ a whole box of them.

3. It's 5 p.m., and Tawnya (be) _____ home from school. Now she (lie)

_____ on the couch in front of the TV. She (watch)

_____ her favorite show, The Simpsons. The only show she (like)

_____ more is The Young and the Restless.

4. When Muhammad (get up) _____ on Saturday morning, he usually (go)

_____ straight to the bathroom. First, he (splash) _____ cold

water on his face, and then he (brush) _____ his teeth. When he gets to the

kitchen, his mother is making herself a pot of coffee, his younger brother (watch)

_____ cartoons on TV, and his father (walk) _____

out the back door with his golf clubs.

5. On Saturday afternoon, Josie usually (go) _____ to the mall. She often has to

wait for her friends. Today, while she (wait) _____ , one friend (walk)

_____ very slowly to the mall. Another friend (put her makeup on)

_____ , and yet another friend (get dressed)

_____ .

6. It's Saturday night, and Murphy (do) _____ what he loves best. He

(watch) _____ a James Bond movie on his new DVD player. Sometimes

his Dad (join) _____ him, but his Dad (be) _____ at a meeting

tonight with his family. They (plan) _____ next month's Christmas

party.

Lesson 34 — Progressive and Non-progressive Verbs

A number of verbs are hardly ever used in a progressive tense. It is hard to explain exactly why, but these verbs rarely sound right when they are in sentences such as,

__✘__ This book **is belonging** to me. (Or) __✘__ I **am forgetting** what my teacher's name is.

To avoid making mistakes with **non-progressive** verbs, all we can do is to memorize them.

be	believe	belong	exist	have*
hate	hear	forget	know	like
love	need	own	possess	prefer
remember	see*	think*	understand	want

*Sometimes, these verbs can be used in the progressive tense (especially "have", "see" and "think") but you must be careful when you do.

The verb "have" can be used progressively when it means to "experience" or "eat", as in "I am having a very bad time at this party." When it means to "own" or "possess", the progressive form is incorrect: "I am having a new CD player" (__✘__).

Also, the verb "think" is only wrong in the progressive tense when it means to "believe", as in "**I am thinking** that the Bulls will win the championship this year" (__✘__). It is entirely all right to use it when you are describing the actual thoughts that are going through someone's head: "**I am thinking** about my lunch right now" (__✔__).

"See" is acceptable when it means "attending on" or "going out with": "I **am seeing** Eric Clapton nowadays for my guitar lessons."(__✔__).

Exercise A. Hold a piece of paper over the chart on this page (scout's honor!), and put an X (__✘__) beside the sentences that do not sound right to you. Put a checkmark (__✔__) beside the sentences that do sound right.

1. _____ Jorge is wanting a glass of water right now.

2. _____ Are you preferring Coke instead of Pepsi?

3. _____ Our teacher is enjoying all the excellent work that we are doing this year.

4. _____ Mariah is hating her boxed lunches.

5. _____ I am needing a bandaid — immediately!

6. _____ Mikey is liking his brand-new Reeboks very much.

7. _____ The defensive end is watching the wide receiver like a hawk.

8. _____ The defensive end is seeing his untied shoelaces.

9. _____ Are we having a good time yet?

Exercise B. The Present Progressive in Different Sentence Types

The present progressive can be used in statements, negative sentences, questions, and short answers.

Statement:
I *am playing* Nintendo right now.
[He / She / It] *is playing* Nintendo right now.
[You / We / They] *are playing* Nintendo right now.

Negative:
I *am not playing* Nintendo right now.
[He / She / It] *is not playing* Nintendo right now.
[You / We / They] *are not playing* Nintendo right now.

Question:
Am I *playing* Nintendo right now?
Is [he / she / it] *playing* Nintendo right now?
Are [you / they] *playing* Nintendo right now?

Short Answer: Yes, I *am*.   Yes, [she / he / it] *is*.   Yes, [you / we / they] *are*.
No, I *am* not. No, [she / he / it] *is* not. No, [you / we / they] *are* not.
{Or}   {I'*m* not.   … *isn*'t.   … *aren*'t.}

Choose two verbs that describe energy and action. For each one, write out a statement, a negative sentence, a question and a short answer in the present progressive tense. Try to add a little spice to your sentences (make them interesting or fun).

Example: Jamal, sing.
1. Jamal *is leaping* over that tall building right now.
2. Jamal *is* not *leaping* over that tall building.
3. *Is* Jamal really *leaping* over that tall building?
4. Yes, he *is*! (I'm not kidding you).

Verb #1.

1. _____

2. _____

3. _____

4. _____

Verb #2.

1. _____

2. _____

3. _____

4. _____

Lesson 35 — Present Perfect Tense

Verb phrases that are called "present perfect" describe a time period that begins in the past and moves right up to the present time. They often **emphasize** an action that started in the recent past and has recently been completed:

> *"I **have** (just) **talked** to Heath Ledger on my cell phone."*

The word "perfect" for this tense is a bit confusing, because most of us think "perfect" means something like getting a perfect score on a test, or having "a perfect day." There is an older meaning of "perfect," though, and that meaning is very similar to "finished" or "completed."

Specifically, the present perfect tense usually describes an action that began in the past, and has recently been completed, or that is still true right up until the present moment.

> Example: *"You have been a Nintendo player for two years."*

This describes a process that began two years ago, and is true right up until the present time.

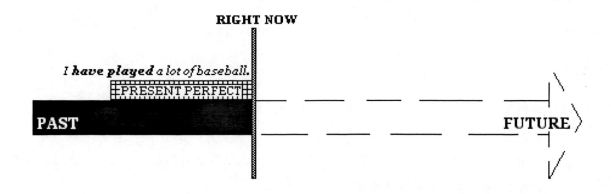

(Present Perfect, continued...)

The present perfect is composed of the helping verb "HAVE" and the Past Participle form of the main verb. This past participle is often in the same form as the simple past form of the verb.

Base form	**Simple Past form**	**Past Participle**
act	acted	acted (as in "has acted"; "have acted")
play	played	played
try	tried	tried

He **tried** to win the championship last year. (**simple past** form; single event in the past)

For seven years now, he **has tried** to win the championship. (**present perfect** form; "HAS" plus "past participle." Seven years ago, up till the present time)

For many verbs, however, there is a difference between the form for the simple past and the form for the past participle. These verbs are called "Irregular."

Base form	**Simple Past form**	**Past Participle**
awake	awoke	awakened
be (is, are)	was, were	been
become	became	become

See the rest of the chart for "Commonly Used Irregular Verbs" on pages 50-51.

Exercise A. Fill in the blanks for the following statements. Then the teacher will go around the room, asking each student for his or her statements.

1. I am a _____ .

2. I **have been** a _____ for _?_ years.
(say something other than "a student.")

Describe something that you have recently done, finished, or accomplished.

3. I **have** just (or "recently") _____ ? (Finished my homework? Eaten lunch?)

Describe something that you have enjoyed for a long time.

4. For as long as I can remember, I **have enjoyed** _____ (homework?)

62

Lesson 36 — Present Perfect, Using Irregular Verbs

Exercise A. Using your own knowledge, a dictionary, or the chart for Common Irregular Verbs on pages 50-51 as a reference, write a correct version of the verb (or verb phrase) in the blanks.

1. Debra has thunk many deep thoughts.

_____

2. I have drank too much.

_____

3. Buffy has slayed the vampire!

_____

4. This cell phone has costed me more money than it's worth.

_____

5. My, how you've grew!

_____

6. Billy has ate his pie.

_____

7. Carmela has spoke in front of the class many times.

_____

8. The bell has ringed and school is out!

_____

9. Franco and Marco have both cutted their fingers today while dissecting those frogs.

_____

Exercise B. Different Sentence Types for the Present Perfect

The present perfect can be used in statements, negatives, questions, and short answers.

Statement: [I / You / We / They] *have helped* a lot of people.
   [He / She / It] *has helped* a lot of people.

Negative: [I / You / We / They] *have* not *helped* a lot of people.
   [He / She / It] *has* not *helped* a lot of people.

Question: *Have* [I / you / we / they] *helped* a lot of people?
   Has [he / she / it] *helped* a lot of people?

Short Answer: Yes, [I / you / we / they] *have.*
   No, [he / she / it] *has not.* (or *hasn't*)

Part One: Choose three irregular verbs from the list on pages 50-51. For each one, write out a statement, a negative sentence, a question and a short answer in the **present perfect** tense. Try to add a little spice to your sentences (make them interesting or fun).

Example: the boss, fly.   1. The boss *has flown* over the cuckoo's nest.
   2. The boss *has* not *flown* over the cuckoo's nest.
   3. *Has* the boss *flown* over the cuckoo's nest?
   4. No, he *has*n't (I was just kidding you).

Irregular verb #1.

1. _____

2. _____

3. _____

4. _____

Irregular verb #2.

1. _____

2. _____

3. _____

4. _____

Irregular verb #3.

1. _____

2. _____

3. _____

4. _____

Part Two: Hunt out three regular verbs — verbs which simply take an "-ed" ending for both the simple past form and the past participle form.

One example is the verb "kick." The simple past tense is "kicked" (as in "He **kicked** the ball at the school wall") and the past participle is also "kicked" (as in "He **has <u>kicked</u>** soccer balls at that wall for as long as he can remember").

As you did in Part One, write out a statement, a negative sentence, a question and a short answer in the **simple past tense** for each of your three regular verbs. Try to add a little spice to your sentences.

Example: Sergio, kick.   1. Sergio *has kicked* many wonderful field goals.
                                            2. Sergio, actually, *has* not *kicked* many field goals at all.
                                            3. So, *has* Sergio *kicked* many wonderful field goals, or not?
                                            4. Yes, he certainly *has*!

Regular verb #1.

1. _____

2. _____

3. _____

4. _____

Regular verb #2.

1. _____

2. _____

3. _____

4. _____

Regular verb #3.

1. _____

2. _____

3. _____

4. _____

Lesson 37 — Subject-Verb Agreement

A subject and a verb need to *agree* with each other in order for a sentence to work. "Agreement" simply means that the verb matches the number and person of the subject.

I **am** at the dance.   [first person, singular]
You **are** at the dance.   [second person, singular]
He (or She) **is** at the dance. [third person, singular]

We **are** at the dance.   [first person, plural]
You **are** all at the dance. [second person, plural]
They **are** at the dance.   [third person, plural]

In the next examples, the subject and the verb **DO NOT** agree with each other :

✘   <u>I **are**</u> at the dance.   **✘**   <u>**You be**</u> at the dance.   **✘**   <u>**They is**</u> at the dance.

1. Mistakes can be made very easily when there is more than one person in the subject:

      ✘   <u>**Gaston and Giselle is**</u> at the dance.
      ✓   <u>**Gaston and Giselle are**</u> at the dance.

2. Phrases that begin with the words "along with" or "together with" do not give the same information that we find in the word "and". These phrases do not change a singular subject into a plural one.

      ✘   <u>**Giselle**</u>, along with Gaston and Geri, <u>**are**</u> at the dance.
      ✓   <u>**Giselle**</u>, along with Gaston and Geri, <u>**is**</u> at the dance.

A good way to check whether your subject and your verb agree is simply to read your work aloud to yourself. Often, a mistake that seems correct when you look at it will sound wrong when you hear it.

3. Be careful with pronouns such as "everybody" and "everyone". They seem to be plural, but they are actually single. Put the word "single" between "every" and "body", or between "every" and "one", and that will emphasize that they are not plural.

      ✘   Everybody <u>**are**</u> here.   **✓**   Everybody <u>**is**</u> here.
          {*Every single body…*}   {*Every single body* **is** *here.*}

4. One more rule: nouns such as *pants, shorts, glasses,* and *scissors,* and are considered plural nouns. The phrase "pair of" often goes in front of them. We say,

     "My pants **are** in the laundry."   *Or*   "Your scissors **aren't** in the cupboard."
     {*"My favorite pair of pants* **are** *there."*} *Or* {*"Your pair of scissors* **aren't** *there."*}

5. Group words such as *team, troupe, pack,* and *gang* look plural, but take singular verbs:

That **team** of acrobats <u>**is**</u> on its way. *Or* That **gang** of thieves <u>**is**</u> dangerous.

Exercise A. Circle the subject of each sentence first, then write an appropriate verb in the space given.

1. Our team _____ leading the game right now.

2. The members of the team _____ planning to win the tournament this year.

3. Coffee, after soda pop and juice, _____ my favorite beverage.

4. Door knobs, along with counter tops and telephones, _____ breeding grounds for germs.

5. Frederika and Reiko _____ friends.

6. At camp, everybody _____ friends with everybody else.

7. The ducks at the lake _____ hoping we'll throw them breadcrumbs.

8. A pack of wolves in the forest _____ stalking a deer.

9. My computer, though less powerful than yours, still _____ cooler games on it.

10. I can't believe that you, my best friend, _____ been seeing my boyfriend behind my back.

11. The drama troupe, consisting of Mark, Mary, and Mica, _____ competing at the state-wide theatre festival.

12. My favorite pants _____ in the wash.

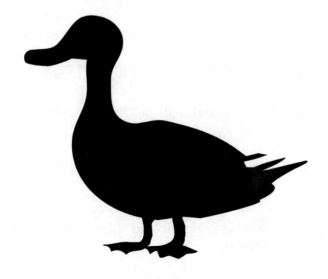

Lesson 38 — Pronouns: Agreement with Gender and Number

When we talk about a girl, we say "she," "her" and "hers."
- ✓ **Brianna** forgot **her** coat at my house.

When we talk about a boy, we say "he" and "his."
- ✓ **Abdul** forgot **his** coat at my house.

When we want to discuss someone whose gender we don't know, we often say "he or she," "his or her," and "his or hers."
- ✓ **Someone** forgot **his or her** coat at my house.

Often, we can make a good guess about the gender of the subject. If the coat looks like a girl's, we would obviously say,
- ✓ **Someone** forgot **her** coat at my house.

Another option is to find some way of restating the idea without mentioning gender.
- ✓ **Someone** forgot **a** coat at my house.

Frequently, people use "they," "them," "themselves," "their," and "theirs" to talk about a singular noun. This is acceptable in informal speech and writing, but it is *not correct* in formal English.
- ✗? **Someone** forgot **their** coat at my house.   (this is informal)

The words "they," "them," "themselves," "their," and "theirs" are all plural, whereas words such as "someone," "nobody," and "whoever" are always singular. You wouldn't say
- ✗ "**Abdul** forgot **their** coat at my house"!

A thing cannot be both plural and singular at the same time. In this way, "themself" cannot be a word, because "them" is plural and "self" is singular.
- ✗ The person who built that wall did it all by **themself**.

Let's take one more look at that last sample sentence, and review the ways that we could correct it.
1. ✓ The <u>person</u> who built that wall did it by **himself or herself**.

2. ✓ The <u>person</u> who built that wall did it by **herself**.
{Perhaps you know that the local wall-builder is female, but you've forgotten her name}

3. ✓ The <u>person</u> who built that wall did it without any help.
{Clever restating of idea without mentioning gender}

4. ✓ The **people** who built that wall did it by **themselves**.
{Change *both* the subject *and* the pronoun to plural forms}

68

Exercise A. Correct the following sentences so that they are either consistently plural or consistently singular. Be as creative as possible in finding solutions!

1. Anyone could have finished their homework on time. _____

_____

2. Whoever stole my car must have done it by themself. _____

_____

3. Your secret admirer didn't sign their name on the card? _____

_____

4. An artist must dedicate themself to their art. _____

_____

5. Everyone will find their soulmate. _____

_____

6. Only one member of this class did not pass their final exam. _____

_____

7. When a person loses their right hand, they must learn to write with their left.

_____

_____

Lesson 39 — Sentence MOSH!

Make funny sentences using the lists below.

For example: The _____ _____ _____ with the _____.
               adjective   subject   present progressive   object

Could become: The <u>desperate</u> <u>vampire</u> <u>is flirting</u> with the <u>mosquito</u>.
Or: The <u>hot</u>   <u>babe</u> <u>is laughing</u> with the <u>ducks</u>.

The words in the lists below are only suggestions — feel free to add your own subjects, verbs, adjectives, and objects. Make sure your subjects and your verbs agree with each other!

SUBJECTS	PRESENT PROGRESSIVE	PRESENT PERFECT	ADJECTIVES	OBJECTS
professor	am/are/is going	have/has been	happy / sad	mosquito
donkey	am/are/is painting	have/has eaten	ugly / cute	football
babe	am/are/is hoping	have/has seen	angry / calm	duck
parents	am/are/is chewing	have/has met	hot/cool	marshmallow
bunny	am/are/is laughing	have/has questioned	wild /tame	girl/boyfriend
girl	am/are/is flirting	have/has jumped	skinny / huge	toes
guy	am/are/is asking	have/has denied	favorite	kid
vampire	am/are/is walking	have/has created	voluptuous	pork pie
class clown	am/are/is dancing	have/has enjoyed	desperate	platypus
psychiatrist	am/are/is watching	have/has married	arrogant	robot

1. The _____ _____ _____ to be elected President.
       adjective   subject   present progressive

2. I _____ a really _____ _____.
     present perfect   adjective   object

3. Delilah _____ her _____ _____.
         present progressive   adjective   object

4. The _____ _____ _____ fighting about _____.
      adjective   subject   present perfect   object

5. Miguel _____ with his _____ _____.
       present progressive   adjective   object

6. If you _____ attacked by a _____, the _____
       present perfect   object   adjective

thing to do is to ask your _____ for help.
                       object

7. The _____ _____ on a _____ _____.
      subject   present progressive   adjective   object

Lesson 40 – Composition   *"Your Perfect Day"*

Write a composition in which you describe your perfect day. Try to use only the three kinds of present tense — simple present, present progressive and present perfect — even though you may need to use other tenses when you are explaining something in more detail. However, you will probably find that you will use the simple present tense for most of your story.

Suggested format:
Divide your story into three parts, or three full paragraphs.

1. Morning. "I get up early in the morning, and listen to the birds singing in the trees. I can smell pancakes frying in the kitchen..."

Start by describing your morning routine: Shower? Bath? Do you have chores to do? Perhaps on your perfect day, your sister or brother has to do all your chores? Favorite breakfast?

Describe activities: TV shows? Saturday morning soccer game? Bus trip to your best friend's house? Fishing trip?

2. Afternoon. "My afternoon begins with my favorite lunch, which is..."

Describe: Trip to the mall? Sports? The big football game at the local stadium? TV? Video games? Visit with friend(s)? Homework for your favorite class?

3. Evening. "My evening begins with my favorite supper, which is..."

Describe: Movie? Trip to arena to watch a hockey game? A good party? A gaming session with your friends?

Suggested conclusion: "My perfect day ends with..."(A huge cup of hot chocolate brimming with marshmallows? Falling asleep just as a great movie comes to an end?)

Note: perhaps your perfect day does not include a morning. You can start your composition by saying, "On my perfect day, I sleep until noon." However, you should still divide your day into three parts. You could try "afternoon, evening, late evening," or "Noon until four o'clock; four until eight; and eight until midnight."

UNIT FIVE — PAST TIME

Simple past. The simple past tense is used to describe actions or situations that began and ended at a specific time in the past.

Yesterday, at 5 p.m., Lee *walked* home.
My sister *sailed* to Florida last week.
In 1922, your teacher **finished** school.

The simple past tense is usually formed by adding "-ed" to the basic form of a verb.
For example, *walk, sail, finish* become *walked, sailed, finished*.

Some verbs have irregular past forms (see the chart on pages 50-51):
Run becomes *ran; win* becomes *won; take* becomes *took*.

Yesterday, at 5 p.m., Kim *ran* home.
Our volleyball team *won* the championship last week.
In 1922, my grandmother *took* her first ride in a motorcar.

The simple past can be used in statements, negative sentences, questions, and short answers.

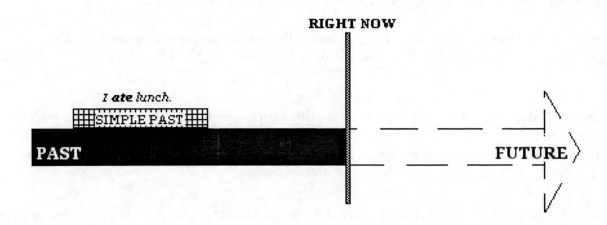

Statement: [I / You / He / She / It / We / They] *studied* last night.

Negative: [I / You / He / She / It / We / They] *did not study* last night.

Question: *Did* [I / you / he / she / it / we / they] *study* last night?

Short Answer: Yes, [I / you / he / she / it / we / they] *did.*
                   No, [I / you / he / she / it / we / they] *did not.* (or *didn't*)

Past Progressive. The past progressive tense is used to **emphasize** that an action that was in progress (taking place, happening) at a particular time in the past.

I *was playing* basketball yesterday afternoon.
My friends *were buying* clothes at the mall last Saturday.

The past progressive tense has two parts: the past form of the verb "BE" in the first part, and the "-ING" form of the main verb.

More examples of the past progressive verb tense:

"I was speaking." "You were calling people." "She was directing the movie."
"He was running to the endzone." "All of you were screaming." "Fans were jumping for joy."

The past progressive is frequently used in a sentence that also uses a simple past tense. The progressive tense describes an action that was in progress when something else happened:

I *was making* a Poptart when you *called*.
You *were running* to the endzone when the referee *blew* his whistle.
Just as my Dad *was starting* his shower, the hot water *ran out*.

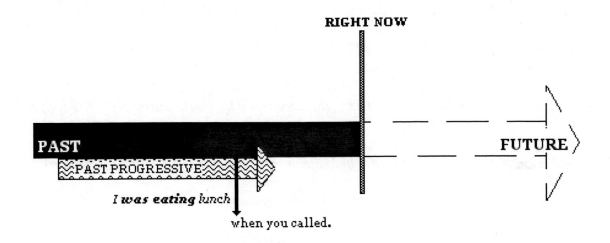

73

Past Perfect. Verb tenses that have "perfect" in their name all emphasize the completion of an action. "Perfect" in this case means "finished" or "completed."

Perfect tenses also describe two times, or two activities. They describe an event or a situation that starts at one time and finishes at a later time. In the **present perfect**, something begins in the past, and is finished or is still true at the **present** time.

> Examples of the present perfect tense:
> *You **have** just **won** your game.* (started two hours ago; is finished right now)
> *She **has been** a teacher since 1977.* (started a few decades ago; is still true today)

The **past perfect** tense usually describes an action that **began in the past**, and then **finished at a more recent point in the past**. The more recent time in the past is usually described in the simple past tense. Examples:

> *You **had** just **won** your game yesterday when the rain **started**.*
> (the game ran from 2 p.m. to 4 p.m., and the rain began at 4 p.m.)

> *She **had been** a teacher for 25 years before she **retired** two years ago.*
> (she was a teacher from 1975 to 2000, when she retired)

The **past perfect** is composed of the helping verb "HAD" (the past form of "HAVE") and the Past Participle form of the main verb. More examples of the past perfect:

> *For seven years, from 1991 to 1998, she **had tried** to win the long jump, but then she switched to the triple jump.*

> *Jeff didn't want a chocolate bar last night, because he **had eaten** three just after supper.*

> *I had eaten lunch when you called.*
> Or   *When you called, I had eaten lunch.*   [see illustration below]

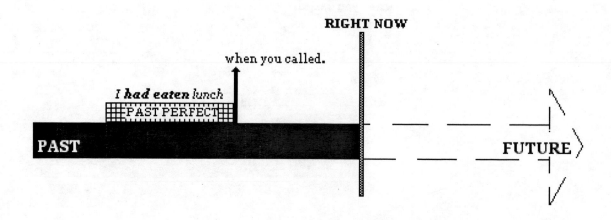

Lesson 41 — Simple Past; Past Progressive; Past Perfect

Exercise A.

Circle the verbs conjugated in the simple past,
underline the verbs conjugated in the past progressive, and
double underline the verbs conjugated in the past perfect.

{Note: there may be more than one verb per sentence!}

1. I had finished breakfast by the time my brother woke up.

2. The fire had started when someone dropped a match at the gas station.

3. Tamara had walked all the way to school before she realized that she had forgotten her

books at home.

4. Caleb was hiking through the swamps when the psychopath confronted him.

5. I watched a movie at Gina's house yesterday.

6. Sheep were not living in New Zealand when the European settlers arrived.

7. The moon was waning as the werewolf returned to his human form.

8. Jimmy had taken 40 pictures before he noticed that his camera had no film in it.

—

Lesson 42 — Simple Past

The simple past tense is used to describe actions or situations that began and ended at a specific time in the past.

> Yesterday, at 5 p.m., the hawk *swooped* down on its prey.
> My sister *travelled* to Florida last week
> In 1942, your teacher *graduated* from university.

The simple past tense is usually formed by adding "-ed" to the basic form of a verb. For example, *talk, fail,* and *wish* become *talked, failed,* and *wished*.

Some verbs, however, have irregular past forms (see the chart on pages 50-51): *run* becomes *ran* (not *runned*); *win* becomes *won* (not *winned*); *take* becomes *took*…

> Yesterday, at 5 p.m., Kim *ate* supper.
> Our volleyball team *lost* the championship last week.
> In 1922, my grandmother *rode* her scooter for the first time.

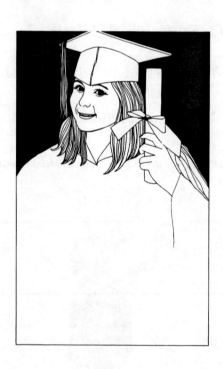

Exercise A. The simple past can be used in statements, negative sentences, questions, and short answers.

Statement: [I / You / He / She / It / We / They] *screamed* last night

Negative: [I / You / He / She / It / We / They] *did not scream* last night.

Question: *Did* [I / you / he / she / it / we / they] *scream* last night?

Short Answer: Yes, [I / you / he / she / it / we / they] *did.*
                      No, [I / you / he / she / it / we / they] *did not.* (or *didn't*)

Part One: Choose three irregular verbs from the list on pages 50-51. For each one, write out a statement, a negative sentence, a question and a short answer in the **simple past** tense. Try to add a little spice to your sentences (make them interesting or fun).

Example: John, sing.   1. John sang in the choir last year.
                              2. John did not sing in the choir last year.
                              3. Did John really sing in the choir last year?
                              4. No, he didn't (I was just kidding you).

Irregular verb #1.

1. _____

2. _____

3. _____

4. _____

Irregular verb #2.

1. _____

2. _____

3. _____

4. _____

Irregular verb #3.

1. _____

2. _____

3. _____

4. _____

Part Two: Hunt out three regular verbs — verbs which simply take an "-ed" ending for both the simple past form and the past participle form.

One example is the verb "play." The simple past tense is "played" (as in "He played guitar") and the past participle is also "played". {Past participles are used in the formation of **all** the tenses with "perfect" in their name, such as "present perfect", "past perfect" and "future perfect".}

As you did in **Part One**, write out a statement, a negative sentence, a question and a short answer in the **simple past tense** for each of your three regular verbs. Try to add a little spice to your sentences.

Example: Samantha, play. 1. Samantha played a mean guitar.
2. Samantha, actually, did not play guitar at all.
3. So, did she or did she not play guitar?
4. Um… yes! She did!

Regular verb #1.

1. _____

2. _____

3. _____

4. _____

Regular verb #2.

1. _____

2. _____

3. _____

4. _____

Regular verb #3.

1. _____

2. _____

3. _____

4. _____

Lesson 43 — Past Progressive

The past progressive tense is used to **emphasize** that an action was in progress (taking place, happening) at a particular time in the past.

> I *was strumming* my guitar yesterday afternoon.
> My friends *were jogging* to the river last Friday.

The past progressive tense has two parts: the past form of the verb "BE" in the first part, and the "-ING" form of the main verb.

> More examples of the past progressive verb tense:
> "I *was singing*." "You *were flipping* burgers." "She *was writing* a funny book."
> "He *was flying* to the endzone." "All of you *were moaning*." "Fans *were shaking* their heads."

The past progressive is frequently used in a sentence that also uses a simple past tense. The progressive tense describes an action that was in progress when something else happened:

> When you *phoned*, I *was doing* my homework.
>   (simple past)   (past progressive)

> You *were flying* to the rim when the center *fouled* you.
>   (past progressive)   (simple past)

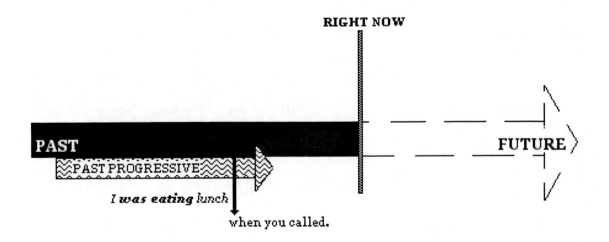

79

Exercise A. Fill in the blanks with the verbs in parentheses.
Use the **simple past** or the **past progressive** tense in each case. In some places, either tense is acceptable.

1.   At 7 p.m., Rachel (do) _____ her homework. It (be) _____ hard

   work, and hard work (make) _____ her hungry. While she (finish)

   _____ her grammar assignment, she (decide) _____

   that she (need) _____ a bag of potato chips.

2.   Rachel (put on) _____ her coat, and (start) _____ to walk

   to the corner store. While she (walk) _____ to the store, a big

   bad wolf (run) _____ up to her and (say) _____ , "Give me all

   your money!"

3.   Rachel (not hear) _____ the wolf, because she (listen) _____

   _____ to her Walkman. She (smile) _____ at him, but

   that (make) _____ the wolf very angry. He was so angry, he (begin)

   _____ to chase his tail. When the police (arrive) _____ ,

   the wolf (still chase) _____ his tail.

4.   Rocky (jog) _____ around the block when he (see) _____ his

   friend Rachel. She (laugh) _____ while the police (put)

   _____ the wolf into the back of the police car.

5.   The police (arrest) _____ the wolf at 7:30 p.m. At 8 p.m., the wolf (sleep)

   _____ in his cell, and he (dream) _____ about

   freedom in a dark, deep forest.

Lesson 44 — Fun with the Past Progressive

Exercise A. One of the best ways to understand the progressive aspect of a verb is to describe someone who *is performing* — or *was performing* — an action.

First, all students will close their books.
The teacher will then command each student in the class to do something. The teacher can start with the list below, but he/she can add other actions. It would be fun to do some brainstorming with the class, and to add another 15 actions to the list.

Teacher: "Danielle, jump up and down... Manuel, do a little dance... Jennifer, look out the window... (and so on)."

1. Sit down slowly.
2. Do a little dance.
3. Look out the window.
4. Celebrate a goal.
5. Stare at your feet.
6. Cheer as if you're at a concert.
7. Flex your biceps.
8. Rap your knuckles on the desk.
9. Scratch your head.
10. Play a bit of air guitar.
11. Repeat a kung fu action.
12. Pretend you're eating an ice cream cone.
13. Hum or whistle something.
14. Make a funny face.
15. Pretend to sharpen a pencil.

Next, the teacher will ask another student to describe what that student *was doing* five or ten minutes ago (using the **past progressive**):

Teacher: "Manuel, what *was* Danielle *doing* a few minutes ago?"
Manuel: "Danielle *was jumping* up and down."

After the teacher has asked everyone to remember one person's action, the teacher can ask if anyone remembers *all* of the actions. Give applause if someone can do it, but only if that student uses the past progressive for each action.

Lesson 45 — Different Sentence Types for the Past Progressive

As you have done in earlier exercises, you will be writing four different kinds of sentences. This time, you can choose any three main verbs that you wish (regular or irregular), but check with a dictionary to make sure that your spelling is correct.

Each sentence (except the short answer) must use a verb phrase that is in the past progressive tense. Try to add a bit of spark or fun into your sentences.

Example: Marco, rollerblade.

Statement:	Marco was rollerblading to the zoo this morning.
Negative:	No, Marco wasn't rollerblading to the zoo.
Question:	Was Marco really rollerblading to the zoo this morning?
Short Answer:	No, he wasn't. (Do I have to repeat myself?)

Verb #1.

1. _____

2. _____

3. _____

4. _____

Verb #2:

1. _____

2. _____

3. _____

4. _____

Verb #3:

1. _____

2. _____

3. _____

4. _____

Lesson 46 — Past Perfect

Perfect tenses describe an event or a situation that starts at one time and finishes at a later time. In the **present perfect**, something begins in the past, and is finished or is still true at the **present** time.

Examples of the present perfect tense:
*You **have** just **finished** your lunch.* (started half an hour ago; is finished right now)
*He **has been** a Sega fan since 1997.* (started a few years ago; is still true today)

The **past perfect** tense usually describes an action that began in the past, and then finished at a more recent point in the past. The more recent time in the past is usually described in the simple past tense. Examples:

*She **had** just **started** her computer yesterday when the power **died**.*
(The computer started at 4 p.m., and the power died at 4:01 p.m., yesterday.)

*Anne **had been** a judge for 30 years before she **resigned** two years ago.*
(She was a teacher from 1970 to 2000, when she retired.)

The past perfect is composed of the helping verb "HAD" (the past form of "HAVE") and the Past Participle form of the main verb. More examples of the past perfect:

*For seven years, from 1991 to 1998, he **had tried** to design a better game than Tomb Raider, but then he decided to program a 3D chess game instead.*

*Joanie didn't play volleyball last night, because she **had run** three miles right after school.*

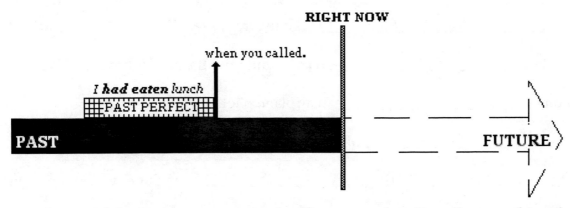

Exercise A. Make up two sentences using the past perfect. Describe something that had happened to you just before something else happened. The teacher might ask you to read one of your sentences out loud to the class.

1. _____

_____

2. _____

_____

Exercise B. Complete the sentences by using the verbs in parentheses in the **past perfect** or the **simple past** tense. The past perfect is often used with words such as "already," "just," "never," "almost," and other expressions relating to time — these words often come between the two parts of the verb phrase, as in "had <u>already</u> eaten" or "had <u>just</u> fainted."

In several places, it is acceptable to use either the **past perfect** or the **simple past**.

1. Jeremy (offer) _____ Jeffery a bite of his sandwich, but Jeffery (already, eat)

    _____ .

2. Maria (just, finish) _____ setting the table when the first guests

    (arrive) _____ for her dinner party.

3. If I (try) _____ a little harder last Thursday, I might have passed that

    exam.

4. For some crazy reason, Jackson (already, read) _____ the

    second chapter of the book before he (start) _____ the first chapter.

5. I (come) _____ too late to the mall. Krusty the Klown (already, give

    away) _____ all the free baseball cards.

6. Janet (be) _____ an astronaut with the NASA program before she

    (become) _____ an airplane pilot.

7. It (snow) _____ all day Friday and most of Saturday. Unfortunately, by

    the time our toboggan party (begin) _____ on Sunday, the snow (already,

    melt) _____ .

8. Last night, we (see) _____ the first game of the World Series between Los

    Angeles and New York. The Dodgers and the Yankees (not play) _____

    against each other for a couple of decades. It (be) _____ a great game!

Lesson 47 — Different Sentence Types for the Past Perfect

As you have done in previous exercises, you will be writing four different kinds of sentences. This time, you can choose any three main verbs that you wish (regular or irregular), but check with a dictionary to make sure your spelling is correct.

Each sentence (except the short answer) must use a verb phrase that is in the past perfect tense — and try to add a bit of spark or fun into your sentences. Also, add a short phrase or clause to the beginning or end of each sentence to indicate the second action and time reference in all "perfect" tenses:

I *had just **finished*** my homework when I ***heard*** the werewolf's howl.
(prior action, time reference — past perfect)   (second, later action — simple past)

By the time I ***got*** back home, my friends ***had drunk*** all the pop.
   (second, later action — simple past)   (prior time reference; prior action; past perfect)

Example:	*(Janelle, run)*
Statement:	By suppertime, Janelle ***had run*** all the way to Mexico.
Negative:	Janelle ***had not run*** all the way to Mexico by suppertime.
Question:	Which is true? ***Had*** she ***run*** all the way there by suppertime, or not?
Short Answer:	Actually, it's true — she ***had***.

Verb #1.

1. _____

2. _____

3. _____

4. _____

Verb #2:

1. _____

2. _____

3. _____

4. _____

Verb #3:

1. _____

2. _____

3. _____

4. _____

Lesson 48 — Irregular Verbs

Exercise A. Using your own knowledge, a dictionary, or the chart of Common Irregular Verbs on pages 50-51 as a reference, write a correct version of the verbs (or verb phrases) in the blanks.

1. That case should have been threw out of court!

_____

2. Windella catched a cold when she goed outside without a coat.

_____

3. Shakespeare was borned in 1564 and writed many plays before he died.

_____

4. When I waked up this morning, my dog had digged a hole in my floor.

_____

5. I knowed it was true because I seen it with my own eyes.

_____

6. Theo had eat many donuts before he knowed he was getting sick.

_____

7. I winned the lottery, but then I losted my ticket.

_____

8. Frank had took his children to the ballgame many times before last night, but he had never saw them making such angry gestures at the umpire.

_____

_____

9. The shark had swimmed half way around the world before it founded a tasty little trout to feed on.

_____

_____

Lesson 49 — Sentence MOSH! Make funny sentences using the lists below.

For example: The _____ _____ _____ with a _____ all day.
adjective   subject   past progressive   object

Could become: The <u>delusional</u> <u>telemarketer</u> <u>was talking</u> with a <u>parrot</u> all day.

Or: The <u>chilly</u> <u>dog</u> <u>was dancing</u> with a <u>barbecue</u> all day.

The words in the lists below are only suggestions — feel free to add your own subjects, verbs, adjectives, and objects. Make sure your subjects and your verbs agree with each other!

SUBJECTS	PAST PROGRESSIVE	PAST PERFECT	ADJECTIVES	OBJECTS
telemarketer	was/were talking	had prepared	weird/normal	poem
genius	was/were sleeping	had eaten	sane/delusional	baseball bat
dog	was/were puking	had wanted	chilly/warm	parrot
sisters	was/were dancing	had yodelled	delicious/disgusting	barbecue
psychopath	was/were writing	had typed	rotten/fresh	breakfast
millionaire	was/were going	had been	perfect/flawed	meat
supermodel	was/were walking	had spoken	fuzzy/harsh	song
geek	was/were hugging	had impressed	beautiful/ugly	journey
mother	was/were nibbling	had cooked	smart/stupid	zoo
chick	was/were hopping	had heard	evil/good	monkey

1. Carlita _____ a _____ _____ when she realized
past perfect   adjective   object

that the _____ was _____.
object   adjective

2. I _____ on a _____ when my _____ walked in.
past progressive   object   subject

3. I _____ a really _____ _____ until I met you.
past perfect   adjective   object

4. Elvis _____ his _____ _____ when he left.
past progressive   adjective   object

5. The _____ _____ _____ to a _____ once.
adjective   subject   past perfect   object

6. The _____ _____ his/her _____ _____ when
subject   past progressive   adjective   object

the most _____ _____ appeared.
adjective   subject

Lesson 50 — Composition   *"A Long Time Ago"*

A. Choose a fun time period from your past that you remember quite well.

Summer (or spring, winter, fall) when you were five years old?
Winter (or spring, summer, fall) two years ago?

Next, write three paragraphs about this time period using this pattern.

      1. What you did in the mornings.
      2. What you did in the afternoons.
      3. What you did in the evenings.

For each part of the day, you could describe all the things that you liked to do.

Sports.
Games.
TV, videos, DVD.
Trips.
Visits (with friends, with members of your family).
Chores at home, or work you did for money.
Food (including snacks).
Band practice.
Hunting or fishing.
Hobbies, crafts, artwork.
Anything you or your teacher can add to this list.

Another way to organize your composition is simply to choose three items from the list above, and write a paragraph about each one.

B. Alternate composition.

Follow the above plan **(A)**, but this time write about someone else in your family. Write about your mother, father, grandmother or grandfather (or write about an older person in your neighborhood). Choose one time period, and then interview him or her. Choose, say, the time when your mother was exactly your age. Ask her what her mornings, afternoons, and evenings were like during the summer holidays, for example.

Use what you learned about direct and indirect quotations. Try to use a few direct quotations from your mom, dad, grandmother or grandfather in your composition.

UNIT SIX — FUTURE TIME

Simple Future: "WILL" and "BE GOING TO"

The future time is expressed most often by a tense called the **simple future.**
It is formed with the helping verb *will* and the basic form of the main verb.

Examples (all referring to next year):

I *will make* the team. You *will be* my agent. She *will coach* me.
I *will run* to the endzone. You *will scream.* My coach *will jump* for joy.

Another verb phrase can be used in place of *"will."* This phrase is *"be going to."*

I *am going to make* the team. You *are going to be* my agent. She *is going to coach* me.
I *am going to run* for glory. You *are going to scream.* My coach *is going to jump* for joy.

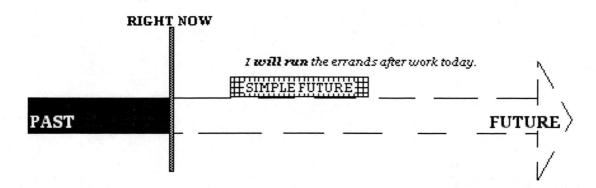

Other helping verbs pointing to the future: *could, should, would, may, might, can, must*

When "will" or "be going to" is used for the future, it implies a **definite time** in the future. Other helping verbs can replace "will," but these words change the meaning (or the mode, or the attitude) of the verb phrase. Some of these "modal" helping verbs are

   could, should, ought to, would, may, might, can, must, have to

These other helping verbs add the ideas of possibility ("could," for example, or "may"), responsibility ("should"), ability ("can") or necessity ("must") to a sentence.

Examples:
I **could run** for the endzone. (The main verb is "run"; the helping or "modal" verb
                  is "could", indicating a possible action.)
I **may run** for the endzone. (I'm still thinking about it.)
I **should run** for the endzone. (This is my responsibility to the team.)
I **must run** for the endzone. (This is a necessary action.)

Future Progressive

The future progressive tense describes an action that will be in progress (taking place, happening) at some future time. This tense is composed of three parts:

>   (b) The helping verb WILL.
>   (c) The helping verb BE.
>   (d) The "-ING" form of the main verb: speak**ing**, call**ing**, direct**ing**, etcetera.

Examples:
I *will be speaking*. You *will be calling* people. She *will be directing* the movie.
I *will be running* to the endzone. You *will be screaming*. My coach *will be jumping* for joy.

The future progressive is frequently used in a sentence that has a second time reference.

You will probably call me at 6 p.m. At that time, I *will be making* my supper.
The defense will fall flat on its face. When they get up, Bo *will be running* to the endzone.
It always happens. When the hot water runs out, you *will be taking* a shower.

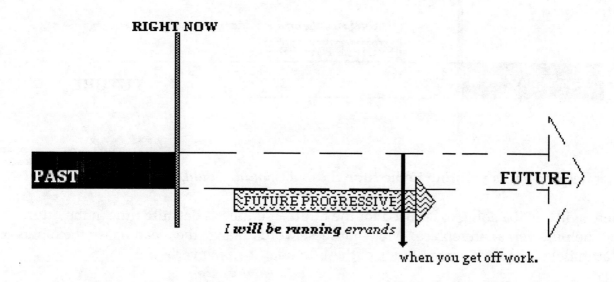

Note: the contraction for "will **not**" is "won't."

Examples: *I will not be running errands. >> I **won't** be running errands.*
*I will not be making my supper. >> I **won't** be making my supper.*

90

Future Perfect

Verb tenses that have "perfect" in their name all emphasize the completion of an action. "Perfect" in this case means "finished" or "completed."

Perfect tenses also describe two times, or two activities. They describe an event or a situation that starts at one time and finishes at a later time.

In the **future perfect** tense, an action or event will be finished or completed before another time, action or event in the future.

Examples:

*By the time we get to Arizona, we **will have eaten** every last one of those tortilla chips.*
*When she graduates next month, Tawanda **will have paid** off all of her loans.*
I have a lot of chores to finish before the game tonight. By the time the game starts,
    *though, I **will have finished** everything I was supposed to do.*

Take one of the example sentences above:
    Students will start a trip to Arizona sometime in the future.
    Single event in the future = arrival of a group of students in Arizona.
    During that future trip, they will snack on tortilla chips.
    The future perfect tense emphasizes the completion of that action (eating all the chips)
    either before or at the same time they get to Arizona.

Future perfect tenses are composed of three parts:
1. The helping verb WILL.
2. The helping verb HAVE.
3. The PAST PARTICIPLE form of the main verb.

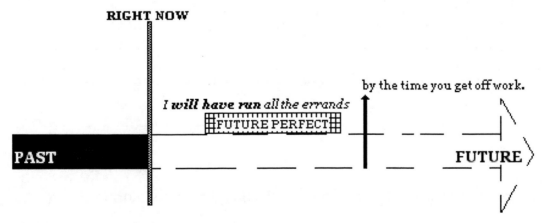

Note: the contraction for "will not" is "won't."

*I will not [**won't**] have run all the errands by the time you get off work.*

91

Lesson 51 — Identifying Future Tenses

Exercise A.   Circle the verbs conjugated in the simple future,
underline the verbs conjugated in the future progressive, and
double underline the verbs conjugated in the future perfect.

{Note: there may be more than one verb per sentence, and there may be an adverb or noun placed between the helping verb and the main verb. Also, the contraction for "will not" is "won't".}

1. Joe will definitely go to college after high school.

2. The Lakers will be playing the Knicks tonight at 7:30.

3. The next time you see your older brother, he will have graduated with his Ph.D.

4. Maria is going to play the lead role in *The Phantom of the Opera* tonight.

5. Kareem will be slamming that basketball down all night long.

6. Before this term is over, all of you will have aced every part of *The Power Slam Grammar*

   Book!

7. Will Franco be late again?

8. Amber Dawn won't be rollerskating again for awhile.

Exercise B.   Correct the verb phrases in the following sentences.

1. Jamal gonna practice his trumpet tonight.

_____

2. Lisa be playing her saxophone at the same time that Bart be practicing his moves on the

skateboard.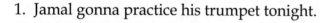

_____

3. Your grandmother gonna be leading the church choir tomorrow morning.

_____

4. Jerrie aint gonna come to the movie tonight.

_____

Lesson 52 — Simple Future: WILL and BE GOING TO

The future time is expressed most often by a tense called the **simple future.**
It is formed with the helping verb *will* and the basic form of the main verb.

Examples (all referring to next year):

I *will be* a philosopher. You *will be* my student. He *will be* our assistant.
I *will discover* the theory of everything. You *will smile.* They *will laugh* at me.

Another verb phrase can be used in place of *"will."* This phrase is *"be going to."*

I *am going to sell* many books. You *are going to be* my agent. She *is going to publish* me.
I *am going to write* a great novel. You *are going to smile.* My fans *are going to love* me.

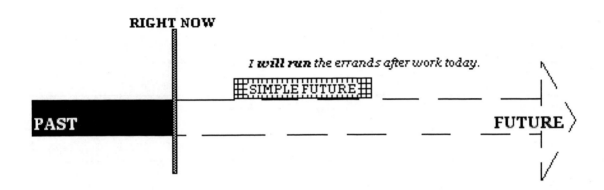

Exercise A. Oral exercise; Contractions

Following the list below, each student in the class will make a sentence about his or her future activities. Give the class two versions of each sentence. In one version, speak every word of your sentence in full. In the second version, use a contraction.

Example: tomorrow.   a. Tomorrow, I will go to my grandma's for supper.
                             b. Tomorrow, **I'll** go to my grandma's for supper.

Or   a. Tomorrow, I am going to go to my grandma's for supper.
                             b. Tomorrow, **I'm** going to go to my grandma's for supper.

1. Later today	2. Tonight	3. Right after school
4. Tomorrow morning	5. Tomorrow afternoon	6. Next week
7. Next month	8. Next year	9. This weekend
10. Sometime soon	11. When I win the lottery	12. Five minutes from now

93

Lesson 53 — Different Sentence Types for the Simple Future

Exercise A. Below, you will be writing four different kinds of sentences. Choose any three main verbs that you wish (regular or irregular), but check with a dictionary to make sure that your spelling is correct.

Each sentence (except the short answer) must use a verb phrase that is in the simple future tense. Try to add a bit of spark or fun into your sentences.

Example: Austin Powers, defeat.

Statement:	Austin Powers *will defeat* Doctor Evil next year.
Negative:	Doctor Evil *will* not *defeat* Austin Powers next year.
Question:	*Will* Austin Powers *defeat* Doctor Evil next year?
Short Answer:	Yes, he really *will*. (or) No, actually, he *will not*. (…he *won't*.)

Verb #1.

1. _____

2. _____

3. _____

4. _____

Verb #2:

1. _____

2. _____

3. _____

4. _____

Verb #3:

1. _____

2. _____

3. _____

4. _____

Lesson 54 — Future Progressive

The future progressive tense describes an action that will be in progress (taking place, happening) at some future time. This tense is composed of three parts:

13. The helping verb WILL.
14. The helping verb BE.
15. The "-ING" form of the main verb: speak**ing**, call**ing**, direct**ing**, etcetera.

Examples:
*I **will be jumping**. You **will be hopping** up and down. The cow **will be leaping** over the moon.*
*I **will be aiming** for the basket. You **will be trying** to block me. The fans **will be cheering** for me.*

The future progressive is frequently used in a sentence that has a second time reference.

*You will probably call me at 6 p.m. At that time, I **will be doing** my homework.*
*The dancers will spin three times. When they stop, J Lo **will be running** onto the stage.*
*It always happens. You **will be taking** a shower when the hot water runs out.*

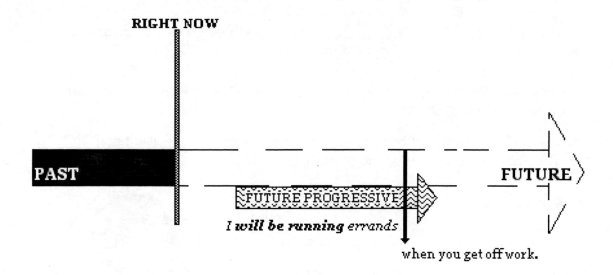

Contractions:

In speech and in informal writing, we often use contractions for our verb phrases.

*I **will be running** errands at 6 p.m.* >> *I'**ll be running** errands at 6 p.m.*

*You **will be hopping** up and down.* >> *You'**ll** be hopping up and down.*

*J Lo **will** not **be running** onto the stage.* >> *J Lo **won't be running** onto the stage.*

Exercise A — Future Progressive. Fill in the blanks with the future progressive form of the verb in parentheses. If you see a "not" beside the verb, write the negative form of the verb phrase. Do not use contractions. (Note: in several cases, the simple future tense will also suit a sentence, but use the future progressive anyway.)

Example. Billy Bob (not, fish) ____*will not be fishing*____ tomorrow morning.

1. The psychic told Geraldine that she (go) _____ on a long journey across the sea.

2. The band (not, sign) _____ autographs at this booth after the show.

3. If you want to know where I am, I (walk) _____ the dog in the park.

4. Because of her accident, Jackie (not, race) _____ go-karts for a long time.

5. Yolanda (talk) _____on the telephone all night unless we stop her.

6. Trajan (babysit) _____ while I go to the hairdresser's.

Exercise B — Contractions. For the first four sentences in **Exercise A**, write out the parts that can be shortened into contractions.

Example: (a) [Billy Bob will not be fishing tomorrow morning.]   ___*won't be fishing*___ .
           (b) [She will be singing at the prom tomorrow.]   __She'll be singing__ .

[1] …she (go) _____

[2] (not, sign) _____

[3] …I (walk) _____

[4] (not, race) _____

Exercise C — Oral. Each person in the class will take turns pretending to be a psychic — someone who can predict the future. Make one prediction about the person who comes after you on the class list. (If there is time, your teacher may allow you to make more than one prediction, or may allow you to make predictions about more than one person.
      Begin by using one of these time phrases:

(a) One year from now, …   (b) Five years from now, …   (c) Ten years from now, …

Example: *"Ten years from now, Carlo will be running the biggest computer company in America."*

Lesson 55 — Different Sentence Types for the Future Progressive

Exercise A. In this exercise, you will be writing four different kinds of sentences. Choose any three main verbs that you wish (regular or irregular), but check with a dictionary to make sure that your spelling is correct.

Each sentence (except the short answer) must use a verb phrase that is in the future progressive tense. Try to add a bit of spark or fun into your sentences.

Example: *our teacher, run* (as in "running for political office").

Statement:	Our teacher *will be running* for mayor next month.
Negative:	Our teacher *will* not *be running* for mayor next month.
Question:	*Will* our teacher *be running* for mayor next month?
Short Answer:	Yes, she really *will*. (or) No, actually, she *will not*. (...she *won't*.)

Verb #1.

1. _____

2. _____

3. _____

4. _____

Verb #2:

1. _____

2. _____

3. _____

4. _____

Verb #3:

1. _____

2. _____

3. _____

4. _____

Lesson 56 — Future Perfect

Verb tenses that have "perfect" in their name all emphasize the completion of an action. "Perfect" in this case means "finished" or "completed."

Perfect tenses also describe two times, or two activities. They describe an event or a situation that starts at one time and finishes at a later time.

In the **future perfect** tense, an action or event will be finished or completed before another time, action or event in the future.

Examples:

*By the time we get home, my father **will have fixed** both the X-Box and the Game Cube.*
*Next week, when he gets out of jail, Frank **will have paid** off his debt to society.*
Sarah has a lot of assignments to write tonight. However, by the time class starts tomorrow,
*   she **will have finished** everything she was supposed to do.*

Take one of the sample sentences above: *By the time we get home, my father **will have fixed** both the X-Box and the Game Cube.*

A couple of students will start to go home at some point in the future.
The end of this future trip is their arrival at one student's home.
During this trip, the father will be working on the video game consoles.
Before they get home, even if it is close to the very same time, the father *will have finished*.
He *will have fixed* the video game consoles.

Future perfect tenses are composed of three parts:
1. The helping verb WILL.
2. The helping verb HAVE.
3. The PAST PARTICIPLE form of the main verb.

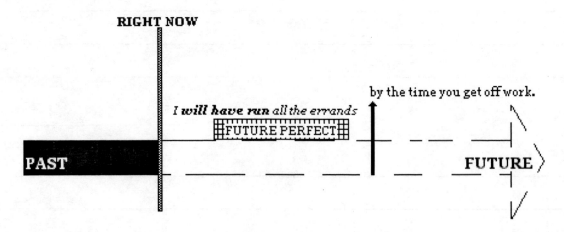

[Negative form] *I will not [**won't**] have run all the errands by the time you get off work.*

98

Exercise A. Future Perfect

Fill in the blanks with the appropriate form of the future perfect verb phrase.
In the second blank, write the contraction form of these phrases.

Example: By the time you get here, she (eat) _____will have eaten_____ all the Oreos.
            [contraction form]   _____she'll have eaten_____ ...

1. I hope that by the time I'm twenty I (travel) _____ all
   over the world.
               [contraction form] _____

2. He (graduate) _____ from college by the time I get
   there.
   [contraction form] _____

3. We (sleep) _____ for approximately one third of
   our lives by the time we die.

   [contraction form] _____

4. If you buy that pair of shoes, you (spend) _____ half
   of your allowance.
               [contraction form] _____

5. By the time you get hungry, I (eat *or* finish) _____ my
   supper.
               [contraction form] _____

Exercise B. Four Sentence Types using the Future Perfect

Make up a fun sentence. Then, using the same idea, create a short dialogue by changing that
sentence into a negative sentence, a question, and a short answer. For example:

Statement: "By this time next year, Zoe *will have recorded* her first CD!"
Negative: "Her rival, Chloe, *will not have recorded* her CD."
Question: "*Will* Zoe *have sold* any copies of that CD?"
Short Reply: "Yes, she *will have!*"

1. Statement: _____

2. Negative: _____

3. Question: _____

4. Short Reply: _____

*{Questions: Do any of your sentences sound awkward? Is it just as easy to use the simple future with your
sentences? Often, one tense can explain your meaning as well as the other one.}*

Lesson 57 — Helping Verbs Similar to "Will" (Modal Verbs)

"Will" is only one helping verb that points to the future time. The verb "will" usually means something like, "definite future", or "no doubt in our mind that this will happen."

There are other verbs that point to the future, but they have different meanings.

Janie *will become* a great basketball player. (no doubt in our minds)
Janie *may become* a great basketball player. (it's possible, but we're not entirely sure)

Janie *will practice* even harder tomorrow. (no doubt)
Janie *should practice* harder tomorrow. (this is our opinion; if she doesn't practice
   harder, we think she is doing something wrong. It could also mean, "If Janie doesn't
   practice harder, she won't do as well as she could in the next game").
Janie *could practice* harder tomorrow. (this could mean two things:
  [a] We think she is able to work harder, and are not sure she is doing all that she can.
  [b] We think, very simply, that she may decide to practice harder tomorrow. It's up to her).

Exercise A. Modal Helping Verbs
There is a blank in front of each of the following sentences. Try out at least three of the helping verbs for each blank. With a partner, talk about the ways in which the meaning changes each time. Use a dictionary if you are not 100% sure of a meaning.

    could, should (*or* ought to), would, may, might, can, must, (*or* have to), will

1. Explain the situation. The teacher _____ understand.

                _____

                _____

2. As soon as my phone is hooked up, I _____ call you.

                _____

                _____

3. While you are on vacation, you _____ write your parents an e-mail every day.

                _____

                _____

4. Our governments _____ do more to save the environment.

                _____

                _____

Exercise B. Modal Helping Verbs

could, should, ought to, would, may, might, can, must, have to, will

Choose the modal helping verb that best fits the following sentences *for you.*
You may add a "not" to your verb phrase, if you wish.

1. I _____ do my homework tonight.

2. Our school's basketball team _____ win the game tonight.

3. I _____ buy a new pair of shoes.

4. When that awful person makes me angry, I _____ scream at him.

5. I _____ eat lots of snacks between meals.

6. Before I go to bed, I _____ brush and floss my teeth.

7. Every day, I _____ try to be a better person.

8. From now on, I _____ do a lot more exercise.

9. We _____ all visit our grandparents more often.

Exercise C. Modal Helping Verbs

Choose one of the modal helping verbs, and make up a sentence. Then, using the same idea, change that sentence into a negative sentence, a question, and a short answer. For example:

Statement: "I *could beat* Kid Jericho in a wrestling match."
Negative: "You *could not beat* Kid Jericho in a wrestling match."
Question: "*Could* Stephanie *beat* Kid Jericho in a wrestling match?"
Short Reply: "Yes, she really *could*!"

1. Statement: _____

2. Negative: _____

3. Question: _____

4. Short Reply: _____

Lesson 58 — Indicating the Future Time with Present Time Verbs

Part One: Simple Present and Future Time Phrases

One of the strangest features of the English language is that we do not always **need** a verb in the "future tense" to indicate future time. Look at the following sentences:

> I *fly* to New York **tomorrow morning**.
> Madonna *comes* to San Francisco **next week**.
> **Tonight**, Dark Angel *loses* her "wings."

All three of these sentences use the **simple present tense**, but all three sentences obviously point to the future. Each sentence does this with a simple expression of time.

You may of course use the **simple future** in each sentence (or even the **future progressive** if you wish to emphasize the ongoing action of the verb), but it is not necessary. Compare the sentences above with the sentences below.

> I *will fly* to New York **tomorrow morning**. (or *"I will be flying..."*)
> Madonna *will come* to San Francisco **next week**. (or *"will be coming"*)
> **Tonight**, Dark Angel *will lose* her "wings."

Exercise A. For each of the following sentences, fill in the blanks with two versions of the verb in parentheses. Use the simple future for the first blank, and the simple present for the second blank.

1. Jerry (see) _____ the eye doctor tomorrow.

   _____

2. This weekend, Martha (go) _____ to New York.

   _____

3. Bleeding Gums Jackson (play) _____ on MTV tonight.

   _____

4. Our football team (go) _____ for the championship this afternoon.

   _____

5. Tomorrow night, the President (make) _____ a very important speech.

   _____

Part Two: Present Progressive and Future Time Phrases

As we pointed out in **Part One** of this lesson, speakers of English do not always **need** a verb in the "future tense" to indicate future time. We have seen how the **simple present** can be used with future time phrases to indicate future time.

The **present progressive** tense can do the same kind of job — as long as there is a future time phrase in the sentence, such as "next week," "tonight" or "tomorrow afternoon."
In many cases, you can choose freely from the simple future, the simple present, or the present progressive. They are all entirely and formally correct. Examples:

	I *will fly* to New York **tomorrow morning**.	(simple future)
	I *fly* to New York **tomorrow morning**.	(simple present)
	I *am flying* to New York **tomorrow morning**.	(present progressive)
Or	I'*m flying* to New York **tomorrow morning**.	(present progressive with contraction)

	Madonna *will come* to San Francisco **next week**.	(simple future)
	Madonna *comes* to San Francisco **next week**.	(simple present)
	Madonna *is coming* to San Francisco **next week**.	(present progressive)
Or	Madonna'*s coming* to San Francisco **next week**.	(present progressive with contraction)

Exercise A. For each of the following sentences, fill in the blanks with two versions of the verb in parentheses. Use the simple future for the first blank, and the present progressive for the second blank.

> Example: Mike (play) **will play** in the pool tournament tomorrow.
>   **is playing** …

1. Donovan (compete) _____ in the marathon this Saturday.

    _____

2. Next term, I (take) _____ Geography with Mrs. Patel.

    _____

3. Sasha and Franz (arrive) _____ on the one o'clock train.

    _____

4. Ramona (move) _____ into her new house this weekend.

    _____

5. Tomorrow, the class (go) _____ on a trip to the zoo.

    _____

Lesson 59 — Review of Tenses: A Contest

Part One — Present Time

1. Divide the class into two teams.

2. Two people from Team A perform an action in front of the class; for example, writing on the chalkboard, sitting on the floor, dancing the tango, or whatever creative plan they decide on.*

3. Members of Team B must accurately guess what the action is, and then they must describe the action in the simple present, the present progressive, and the present perfect. They should also add a time phrase to each sentence to make it clear why they are using a particular tense. If the Team B players succeed, they get a point for each correct tense.

   Examples:

Simple present: "Tony and Maria *write* on the chalkboard **every week**."
Present progressive: "Tony and Maria *are writing* on the chalkboard **right now**."
Present Perfect: "Tony and Maria *have written* on the chalkboard **many times**."

Team A's answers (members of Team B may also wish to write these answers out for practice):

Simple present: _____

Present progressive: _____

Present perfect: _____

4. Then it is Team B's turn to send two players up, and Team A's turn to describe their action. If the Team A players succeed, they get a point for each correct tense.

Team B's answers (members of Team A may also wish to write these answers out for practice):

Simple present: _____

Present progressive: _____

Present perfect: _____

*Note: Your teacher may decide to have Team B perform its action right after Team A performs its action, so that both teams can work on their three sentences at the same time. The teacher may also choose between having each team work in groups, or having individual members of each team make up three sentences of their own.

(Tense Contest, continued…)

Part Two — Past Time

Repeat steps 1 to 4 from Part One, with two different actors from each team. This time, however, each team must describe the actions using three tenses that describe the past. Each team should also add a time phrase to each sentence, especially if it helps to clarify the meaning of a sentence. Examples:

Simple past: "Jak and Jill *scratched* the chalkboard **earlier today**."
Past progressive: "Tony and Maria *were scratching* the chalkboard **five minutes ago**."
Past Perfect: "**Before we yelled at them**, Jak and Jill *had scratched* the chalkboard twice."

Your team's anwers (one point for every correct answer):

Simple past: _____

Past progressive: _____

Past perfect: _____

Part Three — Future Time

For part three, two new members of each team must perform an action. This time, each group must make up **five** different sentences to describe that action **as if** it will happen **in the future**. Use the verb tenses indicated in the parentheses. If you need help, look up the explanations throughout UNIT SIX. One point for each correct answer.

1. (simple future, with "will") _____

_____

2. (simple future, with "be going to") _____

_____

3. (future progressive, "will & be & verb-ing") _____

_____

4. (future perfect, "will & have & past participle") _____

_____

5. (simple present or present progressive with a future time phrase) _____

_____

Lesson 60 — Composition   *"Plans for the Future"*

Write a composition in which you outline your plans for the future. You should divide your composition into three parts, or three subheadings. You can do this by choosing three of the suggested topics or subheadings from the following list:

1. The job you will have. Related to sports? Computers? The movie business? Television? Helping animals (veterinarian)? Saving the environment? Space travel? Running a chain of fast food stores? Helping mom and dad with their business? Music?

2. The house you will have. Indoor swimming pool? IMAX movie screen in the giant living room? Or would you like a very simply, cosy little home?

3. Husband? Wife? Number of children? No children?

4. Pets. Hundreds of cats? A butterfly room? One very tiny dog?

5. Amount of money. Will you be extremely rich? Or will you be happy with enough to get by?

6. Lifestyle. Will you party all the time? Will you be like someone you've seen on "Lifestyles of the Rich and Famous"? Will you keep it simple?

7. Travel. Do you plan to see the world? Which parts of the world do you plan to see? Do you plan to visit every state or province in your own country?

8. Sports. Would you like to keep on playing one or more sports to stay in shape? (If you plan to play a sport for a living, then this category overlaps with Category #1 above.)

9. Transportation. What kind of car would you like to drive? Would you like to own your own boat, or fly your own airplane?

10. Can you think of your own categories? Check with your teacher for approval.

After you have chosen three of these categories, write a full paragraph for each one, using different ways that you have learned to describe the future. Have fun! When you write compositions like this one, you can be anyone you want to be!

ANSWER PAGES

UNIT ONE — SENTENCE STRUCTURE

Lesson 1A.
1. 1,3,8,4,4,1,7,8,1.
2. 1,3,4,6,2,3,8,4,1.
3. 8,1,3,4,6,2,3,8,1,7,1.
4. 3,5,7,8,1,6,3,4,4,4,1,7,2.
5. 1,6,1,3,10,1,8,1,7,1.
6. 1,5,3,10,3,1,7,2,1.
7. 9,2,4,1,3,4.
8. 8,1,3,5,4,1,7,8,1,6,8,1,3,5,4,1.

Lesson 2A.
1. Malika - Subject; babysits - Verb; her cousins - Ending.
2. The table - S; collapsed - V. 3. The Galleria - S; is - V; in Texas - E.
4. Jorjia - S; plays - V; paintball - E. 5. The cowboy - S, saddled - V, his horse - E.
6. Darryl - S; has - V; a new Discman - E.
7. Tanya - S; is - V; a great figure skater - E.

Lesson 2B.
1. The wolf - Subject; howled - Verb; at the moon - Ending (and) the campers - Subj.; shivered - Vb
2. I - S; like - V; orange juice - E; (but) my sister - S; prefers - V; grape juice - E
3. Boots - S; purrs - V; (while) Buttons - S; chases - V; birds - E.
4. Andrew - S; likes - V; Andrea - E; (but) Andrea - S; likes - V; Albert - E.

Lesson 3A.
1. ...their leaves. 2. because she... 3. his day off... 4. because it...

Lesson 4A.
✓ = 1, 6, 8. ✖ = 2, 3, 4, 5, 7.

Lesson 6A. (many possible correct revisions)
1. I asked Molly to go to the movies with me but she said no. Then I asked Holly to go to the movies with me, but she said she was sick. I even asked Polly to go to the movies with me, but she said was moving to Alaska. In the end, I asked Danika, and she said yes.
2. Yesterday I went to the mall and bought a basketball. Then I took it over to my friend Shauna's house so that we could shoot some hoops. After that, I went home and ate supper.
3. I meant to call you Friday night but I couldn't use the phone. First my mom was talking to her sister who lives in Japan. Then my brother went on-line and refused to get off the Internet.

Lesson 7A (possible answers).
1. and; 2. but; 3. while; 4. so; 5. although; 6. and; 7. but/and.

Lesson 8A.
1. ...and watched a movie.
2. ...as talking about TV.
3. ...and because we all drink the same water... {Or} Because we all farm the same land, breathe the same air, and drink the same water, we have a responsibility...
4. In this scene, Carlos will play the Cyclops, Angie will play Hera, Natasha will play Io, and Gordon will play Zeus.
5. We need to reach out to the people who do not have food, the people who do not have homes, and the people who do not have hope. {Or} We need to reach out to the people who do not have food, homes, or hope.
6. My hobbies are snowboarding, playing basketball, and hanging out with my friends.

Lesson 9.

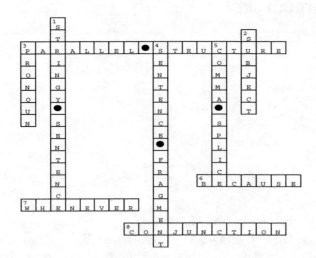

UNIT TWO — QUESTIONS, QUOTATIONS and PRONOUNS

Lesson 12A. 1. can't you? 2. doesn't she? 3. aren't they? 4. does he? 5. aren't you?
6. will they? 7. isn't it? 8. is it? 9. haven't you? 10. would you?

Lesson 13A.
1. Rajid shouted, "Look out! That truck is coming right for us!"
2. My grandmother always says, "Count that day lost in which you have learned nothing."
3. "If I'd known we were going to the beach," said Joan, "I would have brought my swimsuit."
4. "One day I'd like to fly an F22 Raptor," Marjorie said thoughtfully.
5. "Does anyone want to go see a movie?" Dad asked. "I'll pay for it."
6. "My guitar lesson isn't until five," Moanda said. "We still have an hour."

Lesson 13B.
1. Kieran asked, "Could you give me some money to rent a video game?"
2. My grandfather always says, "If it's worth doing, do it well."
3. "Next Tuesday," said Ms. Garcia, "there will be a math test."
4. "I wish we could go to the cottage this weekend," moaned Susie.
5. "Let's order some pizza," said Mike. "I'm starving."
6. "I wonder," Ajani said, looking up from his book, "if people…"

Lesson 14A.
1. Uncle Jimmy asked, "How old are you now?"
2. "Let's try out for the band this year," Harley said to Hank.
3. "Next summer," Juanita said happily, "we're going to Jamaica for a month."
4. "I hope you have all enjoyed this evening's presentation," said the emcee.
5. "Ho ho ho," chuckled Santa. "Merry Christmas!"
6. Maxine asked, "Could we buy a CD burner?"
7. As Juliet puts it, "A rose by any other name would smell as sweet."
8. "There's something wrong with your funny bone," frowned the doctor.
9. "Hey," Mom said, "just where do you think you're going?"
10. Kareem said, "Let's get an ice cream as soon as the game is over."
11. "I promise not to lie this time," the politician said.
12. "On the quiz," the teacher informed the class, "there will be ten multiple choice questions."

Lesson 15A. (many possible answers)
1. Tallulah whispered to Kay that she should not be afraid, because all the bears were hibernating at that time of year.
2. My neighbor told me that, with all the awful things happening right now, the world was rapidly going to a very dark place.
3. Mr. Dutell said that he hated how long it took for his screen to load up completely after he first clicked his mouse.

Lesson 16A.
1. That is my neighbors' fence.   2. That is Harvey's guitar.
3. One cat is Martha's and the other is Larry's. (OR) Those cats are Martha's and Larry's.
4. This is my mother and father's store.
5. Would you like to go swimming in my grandparents' pool?
6. Have you tried Billy's recipe for Texas-style BBQ sauce?
7. The green station wagon is my uncle's and the red convertible is my aunt's.
8. This business's accounts need to be reorganized.

Lesson 16B.
1. Welcome to the amusement park that Gary and Harry own.
2. One pair of pants belongs to Polly and the other pair belongs to Esther.
3. Why are the cats belonging to Franklin and Shania so cute?

Lesson 17A. 1. your; 2. our; 3. hers; 4. my; 5. yours; 6. theirs; 7. her; 8. mine; 9. his; 10. ours
Lesson 17B. 1. his 2. their 3. hers 4. theirs.

Lesson 18A. √ = 1, 3, 4, 7, 12.   X = 2, 5, 6, 8, 9, 10, 11.
Lesson 19. Crossword Puzzle

UNIT THREE — COMMANDS and DICTION

Lesson 22A. (other answers are possible)
1. The sergeant commanded his troops to drop and give him fifty push-ups.

2. Marco yelled at Pat to watch out for the guy with the gun.
3. Benny told Crystal that drinking some soda would make her stomach ache go away.
4. The hippie told the officer that making love was better than making war.
5. Mr. Chu ordered a kid to get down from a tree.
6. Ursuline teased her older brother about taking his mom to the prom.
7. Mrs. Jetson told her daughter that she should buy some nice clothes with her birthday money.

Lesson 23A. (other answers are possible)
1. "Stop, drop, and roll if you ever catch on fire," the fireman instructed the children.
2. "Buy a present for your father's birthday," Mrs. Li reminded her son.
3. The card Rochelle had picked up said, "Do not pass GO or collect 200$."
4. "Walk down Third Street and turn right on Blair," Tyrell instructed the lost child.
5. Kassandra yelled, "Call the police!"
6. "Go to your room and think about what you've done," Jocko's parents ordered him.
7. "Bring soda pop, chips, and candy to the picnic," Hailey told her friends.
8. "Stay calm, ignore insults, and walk away if you want to avoid fighting," Salem told his brother.

Lesson 24A. (other answers are possible)
1. "Could you kids please get off my property?"
2. "Mom, do you think you might be able to buy me a mountain bike?"
3. "Could you please separate your dog from mine?"
4. "Young man, would you please go to your room right now?"
5. "Could you slow this car down, please?
6. "If you don't mind, could you please stop picking your nose in public?"
7. "Could you say something a little more interesting?"
8. "Would you please pick up that phone?"
9. "Could you eat that meatloaf, please?"
10. "Would you mind leaving me alone?"
11. "Fluffy -- could you please stop twinkling on the neighbor's lawn?"

Lesson 25A. I'd; won't; it's; don't; you're.
Lesson 25B. 1. doesn't; 2. they're; 3. wouldn't; 4. it's; 5. Haven't; 6. don't; 7. won't;
         8. You've; 9. Let's; 10. That's.

Lesson 26A. Suggestions: 1. calm down; relax.   2. police officer.
3. How are you? (or) What is going on right now?   4. is not.   5. boy / man / young gentleman.
6. attractive person.   7. disappointment.   8. That is unfortunate.   9. attractive / excellent.
10. Let us leave / depart.

Lesson 27A. Suggested answers. 1. Where are you? 2. He is my best friend.
3. I am happy because I am going to Japan for a month. 4. What are you doing this weekend?
5. Did you go see a movie? 6. I am relaxing. 7. Aren't you coming? / Are you not coming?
8. This is my first day off in a month, so I am going to enjoy it. 9. She ate my French fries.
10. I am not going to argue with you, because you are too stubborn.
11. If you can't say anything nice, keep quiet. 12. Who is/was there?
13. Clarrissa is my mother's cousin. 14. You broke my window! 15. You are powerful & respected.

Lesson 29A. (Many possible answers.)
Patti and I went to the beach last Saturday to tan ourselves. As we were laying out our towels, I noticed a boy surfing. I brought Patti's attention to the really attractive surfer, and told her I was

going to flirt with him. Patti wished me good luck. So, when he came out of the water, I walked up to him and told him his father was a thief. He was confused, so I explained that his father had stolen the stars from the skies and put them in his eyes. He responded that my line was staler than my breath, and recommended that I purchase some gum! I could not believe that he would be so rude to me!

UNIT FOUR — PRESENT TIME

Lesson 31A. 1. progressive; 2. perfect; 3. simple; 4. progressive; 5. perfect; 6. progressive; 7. perfect; 8. simple; simple; 9. simple.

Lesson 32A. 1. takes, rides; 2. listen, talk; 3. are; 4. go, travel, drive; 5. like, love, hate, despise; 6. swims; 7. walks; 8. marks; 9. play; 10. order, eat, have; 11. asks, answers; 12. is; 13. know; 14. reads.

Lesson 33B.
1. is; is dancing. 2. loves; is sitting; is eating. 3. is; is lying; is watching; likes.
4. gets up; goes; splashes; brushes; is watching; is walking.
5. goes; waits/is waiting; is walking; is putting her makeup on; is getting dressed.
6. is doing; is watching; joins; is; are planning.

Lesson 34A. ✘ = 1, 2, 4, 5, 6, 8.   ✓ = 3, 7, 9.

Lesson 36A. 1. has thought; 2. have drunk; 3. has slain; 4. has cost; 5. you've grown; 6. has eaten; 7. has spoken; 8. has rung; 9. have both cut.

Lesson 37A. 1. is; 2. are; 3. is; 4. are; 5. are; 6. is; 7. are ; 8. is; 9. has; 10. have; 11. is; 12. are

Lesson 38. Many possible answers. 1. Anyone could have finished *the / this* homework on time. 2. Whoever stole my car must have done it *alone / by himself or herself*. 3. Your secret admirer didn't sign *a / his or her* name on the card? 4. *Artists* must dedicate *themselves* to *their* art. / An artist must be dedicated to creating art. 5. Everyone will find *a* soulmate. / Everyone *has a* soulmate. / *All people* will find *their* soulmates. 6. Only one member of this class did not pass *the* final exam. 7. When *you* lose *your* right hand, *you* must learn to write with *your* left. / If a person loses *his or her* right hand, *he or she* must learn to write with *the* left. / When *people* lose their right hands, they must learn to write with their left hands.

UNIT FIVE — PAST TIME

Lesson 41A. 1. past perfect, simple past; 2. past perfect, simple past; 3. past perfect, simple past, past perfect; 4. past progressive, simple past; 5. simple past; 6. past progressive, simple past; 7. past progressive, simple past; 8. past perfect, simple past, simple past.

Lesson 43A.
1. was doing; was; made / was making; was finishing; decided; needed.
2. put on; started; was walking; ran; said.
3. did not hear; was listening; smiled; made; began; arrived; was still chasing.
4. was jogging; saw; laughed/was laughing; were putting.
5. arrested; was sleeping; was dreaming.

Lesson 46B.
1. offered; had already eaten. 2. had just finished; arrived.   3. had tried.

4. had already read; started.   5. came/had come; had already given away.
6. had been; became.   7. snowed; began/had begun; had already melted.
8. saw; had not played; was.

Lesson 48A. 1. should have been thrown; 2. caught, went; 3. was born, wrote;
4. woke up, had dug; 5. knew, had seen/saw; 6. had eaten, knew; 7. won, lost.
8. had taken, seen; 9. had swum, found;

UNIT SIX — FUTURE TIME

Lesson 51A. 1. simple future; 2. future progressive; 3. [simple present], future perfect;
4.   simple future [BE + Going to]; 5. future progressive; 6. [simple present], future perfect;
7. Simple future; 8. Future progressive.

Lesson 51B. 1. is going to practice / will practice; 2. will be playing; will be practicing;
3. is going to lead / will lead; 4. is not going to come / will not come.

Lesson 53A. 1. will be going; 2. will not be signing; 3. will be walking; 4. will not be racing;
5. will be talking; 6. will be babysitting.

Lesson 53B. 1. she'll be going; 2. won't be signing; 3. I'll be walking; 4. won't be racing.

Lesson 56A. 1. I will have traveled / I'll have traveled; 2. He will have graduated / He'll have
graduated; 3. We will have slept / We'll have slept; 4. you will have spent / you'll have spent;
5. I will have eaten / I'll have eaten.

Lesson 58 Part One A. 1. will see / sees; 2. will go / goes; 3. will play / plays; 4. will go /
goes; 5. will make / makes

Lesson 58 Part Two A. 1. will compete / is competing; 2. will take / am taking; 3. will arrive
/ are arriving; 4. will move / is moving; 5. will go / is going